The Ashes

The Ashes

The Ashes

THE ASHES
THIS THING CAN BE DONE

Story of The Ashes where all the Tests are 'Drawn'

by

Arunabha
Sengupta

Maha
#smahaart

CricketMASH

The Ashes

The Ashes: This Thing Can Be Done
By
Arunabha Sengupta and Maha
Published by CricketMASH
Amstelveen, Netherlands
www.cricmash.com
March 2022

The illustrations of this book are interpretations of cricket, cricketers
and cricket-related events, reconstructed from contemporary
records of the same. In the rare cases when photographs not in
the public domain have been directly used for depicting the event
or action, proper care has been taken to acquire permission
or purchase copyright for the same wherever necessary.

CricketMASH

Maha and Arunabha Sengupta
would like to dedicate the book to
Peter Wynne-Thomas

And

Maha to
her father
M K Ganesh

Arun to
Coco

The Ashes

FOREWORD
Stephen Chalke

It is nearly 140 years since the Sporting Times printed its mock obituary of English cricket - 'the body will be cremated and The Ashes taken to Australia' - and since those ladies in Melbourne presented in jest to the Honourable Ivo Bligh their little ash-filled urn. International sporting contests were in their infancy, the teams selected with no great formality, and neither those ladies at Rupertswood nor 'Bloobs' of the Sporting Times can possibly have imagined how their jests would in time help to mould and define a rivalry that would become one of the enduring high points of a global sporting calendar awash with money.

So much of cricket has changed in the past fifty years, some of it almost beyond recognition. A game once famous for its slow, silent pace, spread across long days, has recreated itself as a noisy, frenetic spectacle compressed into two or three hours. Traditionalists are filled with foreboding about the future of Test cricket and of the long-form game, as the pace of everyday life quickens and the game of football extends its world-wide domination. Yet somehow, in the midst of all this change, one cricketing contest - the Ashes - survives in much the same format as it was a century ago and as popular as ever: England against Australia, a five-Test series, home and away every four years. That little urn remains cricket's greatest prize.

One-day internationals and T20s quickly merge one into another, the detail soon forgotten. Test matches come so thick and fast that they become a blur - but not the Ashes, never the Ashes. For cricket lovers, certainly those in England and Australia, the moments of drama and of high achievement stay fresh in the memory.

Just as I know where I was when I heard of the deaths of JFK and Martin Luther King, can still see myself in the garden looking at the moon where Neil Armstrong was taking his first step, so I can recall vividly my childhood disbelief at England's capitulation at Old Trafford in 1961, the mixture of grief and joy sitting with my dying mother as Bob Willis tore through the Australian batting at Headingley in 1981, the late night with a high temperature when I stayed up with the radio to hear Geoff Miller holding the ricocheted catch that won the 1983 Melbourne Test by three runs.
Long ago but not forgotten.

Before my time, but somehow almost as vivid in my memory, are Hirst and Rhodes scoring those last 15 runs, Hobbs and Sutcliffe batting on a gluepot at The Oval, Larwood's fearsome fast bowling, Bradman's last duck and the Typhoon Tyson. Cricket at its very keenest, its most dramatic.

So here we have a cartoon history of this great contest, capturing all these great moments and many more, right forward to the present. It is conceived by Arun Sengupta, a cricket historian with a tremendous capacity for research and a fertile imagination capable of finding new ways to explore the familiar.

His novella *Sherlock Holmes and the Birth of The Ashes* was a triumph of invention, recreating the world of late Victorian London with great playfulness.

His *Apartheid: A Point to Cover* took a well-worn subject and created a thoroughly original book.

And now, with the aid of illustrator Maha, he has turned his inventiveness to The Ashes, exploring its history with a fresh pair of eyes - and not just one pair of eyes but three: the fan, the romantic and the scholar. Through these pages they each make their own interpretations, a lovely device. Ultimately, though, all four are in love with the game and its history - and there is no better subject for them to explore in this way than the Ashes.

Three cheers for 'Bloobs' and those Melbourne ladies.

PREFACE
Neil Robinson

Like many of my generation my passion for cricket was ignited one summer's day in 1981. The date was Tuesday 21 July, the final day of the Headingley Test match between England and Australia and in my mind's eye I can still see clearly Bob Willis tearing down that hill at the Kirkstall Lane end on his way to 8 wickets for 43 runs as England completed one of the most remarkable comebacks in the history of cricket.

As a match it had everything: momentum that shifted first one way, then the other, leading to a thrilling climax, the romance of a seemingly beaten team coming back from an impossible deficit, and also a hint (but no more than a hint) of the darker elements that have often dogged cricket's steps when the outlandish odds of 500-1 against an England victory tempted players on both sides to consider betting on the outcome.

These three elements – dramatic cricket, the romance of the game and the sometimes dubious actions of its protagonists - are recurring themes throughout this book. Sometimes complementary, often contradictory, they combine to deliver the rich history of one of the most famous and longstanding contests in the sporting world. Any effort to tell the true story of an event, historical or otherwise, is fraught with danger. The historian frequently has to deal with conflicting testimony from those involved and a paucity of actual evidence to corroborate any particular version. The origin of the Ashes urn is a prime example of this. Several different versions of the tale have been presented over the years, some more plausible than others, but none with an iron-clad claim to being definitive. In such cases all the historian can do is to present the likeliest case as he sees it while leaving the field open for other views, which is exactly what Arunabha Sengupta does here.

It is often said of journalists that they never let the facts get in the way of a good story. In this book the facts, harsh though they sometimes are, provide just as entertaining a story as any more romanticised version might have it. The history of cricket is full of controversies and disreputable behaviour, from the gambling and match fixing that afflicted the game at the end of the 18th century to the sandpaper scandal of early 2018. Ashes cricket is no exception to this; witness Bodyline or the throwing scandal of 1958-59, or even WG Grace's run-out of Sammy Jones at the Oval in 1882.

In the face of all these episodes it might be hard to
maintain a romantic view of cricket as a gentleman's game played to
the highest moral standards. But the fact that cricket has often fallen
short of the high moral values it espouses need not invalidate its moral
ambition, nor need it decrease our affection for the game. Perfection,
or the appearance of perfection, can be easy to admire, but it is difficult
to love. If I had to imagine a character personifying cricket he would
probably be a well-mannered, entertaining gentleman of a certain age
who is also a bit of a rogue. i think I prefer him that way.

Arunabha Sengupta's commitment and diligence in tracking down the truth
behind the history of Ashes cricket is commendable, and the result is a
balanced and entertaining work full of surprising facts and details, made
all the more engaging by Maha's wonderful illustrations.

I am delighted to have been asked to write this preface, and hope you
will enjoy the book as much as I have.

The Ashes

AUG 1882
WHEN GIANTS CLASHED,
SPARKS FLEW ...

AND THE ASHES WERE BORN.

ENGLAND SET OUT TO SCORE 85 IN THE FOURTH INNINGS. WG GRACE LED THE WAY WITH 32, BUT THEN WICKETS TUMBLED. ACE BATSMAN CT STUDD WAS HELD BACK IN HIS SLEEVE BY CAPTAIN A.N. 'MONKEY' HORNBY ... AND IN HIS SLEEVE HE REMAINED.

TED PEATE

WHAT IS IT WORTH A WIN WHEN ONE COMES FACE TO FACE WITH ETERNITY?

SOON STUDD WOULD GIVE UP CRICKET AND BECOME A MISSIONARY.

STUDD WAS UNBEATEN ON 0, AT THE NON-STRIKER'S END, WHEN LAST MAN TED PEATE HEAVED ACROSS THE LINE AND WAS BOWLED. ENGLAND WERE ALL OUT FOR 77

I COULDN'T TROOST MAISTER STOOD

FOR ONE SPECTATOR THE TENSION WAS A BIT TOO MUCH. HE COLLAPSED TO DEATH FROM EXCITEMENT.

AND ANOTHER SUPPOSEDLY GNAWED RIGHT THROUGH THE HANDLE OF HIS UMBRELLA

> In Affectionate Remembrance
>
> OF
>
> # ENGLISH CRICKET,
>
> WHICH DIED AT THE OVAL
>
> ON
>
> ## 29th AUGUST, 1882,
>
> Deeply lamented by a large circle of sorrowing friends and acquaintances.
>
> ___
>
> ## R.I.P.
>
> ___
>
> N.B.—The body will be cremated and the ashes taken to Australia.

AS WG LAMENTED AND THE AUSTRALIANS CELEBRATED, IN *SPORTING TIMES* REGINALD SHIRLEY BROOKS (BLOOBS) COMPOSED THE FAMED MOCK OBITUARY.

I LEFT SIX MEN TO SCORE 30-ODD RUNS...

THUS THE LEGEND WAS BORN — AND WAS NURTURED BY A LOVE STORY.

THE LEGEND OF THE ASHES – CRICKET'S IMMORTAL LOVE STORY

1882-83 HON. IVO BLIGH TOOK HIS MEN TO AUSTRALIA IN THE 'QUEST TO REGAIN THE ASHES' THE JOURNEY WAS PERILOUS. OFF THE COAST OF COLOMBO, THE SHIP CARRYING THE PLAYERS, *THE PESHUWAR*, COLLIDED WITH ANOTHER PASSENGER VESSEL, *THE GLENROY.*

TWO YEARS LATER, ACE BOWLER FRED MORLEY DIED OF INTERNAL INJURIES SUSTAINED DURING THE ACCIDENT.

AUSTRALIA WON THE FIRST TEST. BUT ENGLAND CAME BACK IN THE SECOND AS BILLY BATES PICKED UP 14 WICKETS. THEY WON THE THIRD TEST AS WELL, THUS CLINCHING THE SERIES 2-1 AND 'REGAINING THE ASHES'

WHAT THIS BOOK IS ABOUT...

The Ashes

1861-61 -1881-82
PREHISTORY

AS WE HAVE ALREADY SEEN, 'THE ASHES' WAS BORN ON THE LATE
AFTERNOON OF A MURKY AUGUST DAY IN 1882 AT THE OVAL.

HOWEVER, ANGLO-AUSTRALIAN CRICKETING RELATIONS STARTED EARLIER THAN THAT.

THE FIRST OVERSEAS TOUR UNDERTAKEN BY THE ALL-ENGLAND TRAVELLING ELEVEN
WAS IN 1859, AND IT WAS TO NORTH AMERICA.
YES, EVEN AS THE BASEBALL CRAZE WAS TAKING ROOT IN THE NEW WORLD,
PROFESSIONAL ENGLISH CRICKETERS WERE BUSY SPREADING THE GOSPEL OF CRICKET.

THE FIRST VISIT BY AN ENGLISH SIDE TO THE
AUSTRALIAN COLONIES TOOK PLACE IN 1861-62.

THE GREAT NOVELIST, CHARLES DICKENS, PLAYED A RATHER IMPORTANT,
ALBEIT PASSIVE, ROLE BEHIND THE PIONEERING VENTURE.

DOWN THE YEARS, PLAYERS SAILED BOTH WAYS, IN TEAMS OF VARIOUS INTERESTING
COMPOSITIONS. THE GREAT GAMES OF CRICKET, WHICH BECAME KNOWN AS
THE FIRST EVER TEST MATCHES, TOOK PLACE IN MELBOURNE IN MARCH, 1877.

THE BIRTH OF THE ASHES SHOWDOWN AT THE OVAL IN 1882 WAS
THE 9TH TEST MATCH BETWEEN ENGLAND AND AUSTRALIA.

GEORGE PARR'S SIDE, WITH EM GRACE AMONG THEM, TOURED IN 1863-64

THAT'S GRACE BEFORE THE ACTUAL DINNER.

DOWN THE YEARS ENGLISH TEAMS CONTINUED TO TOUR AUSTRALIA. SOME OF THE ENGLISH CRICKETERS LIKE CHARLES LAWRENCE AND WILLIAM CAFFYN STAYED BACK TO PROVIDE COACHING FOR THE LOCALS.

THE FIRST AUSTRALIAN SIDE TO TOUR ENGLAND WAS IN 1868, AND IT WAS A SIDE OF ABORIGINAL CRICKETERS. SOME OF THEM LIKE JOHNNY MULLAGH WERE SUPERB CRICKETERS

THE WORLD HAD TO WAIT TILL 1996 BEFORE JASON GILLESPIE BECAME THE FIRST MALE ABORIGINAL TEST CRICKETER

BLACK MEN IN CRICKET, WHAT NEXT?

WAIT 100 YEARS AND SEE WHAT ANOTHER COLOURED MAN DOES IN 1968

NOSTRADAMUS

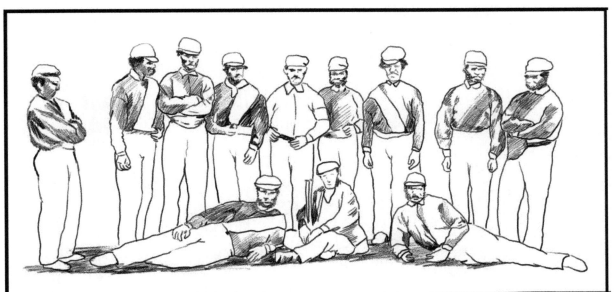

DURING BREAKS, THE CRICKETERS PERFORMED INDIGENOUS ATHLETIC FEATS — BOOMERANG THROWING, BACKWARDS RUNNING, STANDING HIGH JUMPS.

ALL THE ABORIGINALS HAD BEEN GIVEN SIMPLER ANGLICISED NAMES FOR THE BENEFIT OF THE ENGLISH.

JOHNNY MULLAGH — TRADITIONAL NAME: UNAARRIMIN
BULLOCKY — TRADITIONAL NAME: BULLCHANACH.
SUNDOWN — TRADITIONAL NAME: BALLRIN
DICK-A-DICK — TRADITIONAL NAME: JUNGUNJINANUKE
JOHNNY CUZENS — TRADITIONAL NAME: ZELLANACH
KING COLE — TRADITIONAL NAME: BRIPUMYARRIMIN
RED CAP — TRADITIONAL NAME: BRIMBUNYAH
TWOPENNY — TRADITIONAL NAME: MURRUMGUNARRIMAN
CHARLEY DUMAS — TRADITIONAL NAME: PRIPUMUARRAMAN
JIMMY MOSQUITO — TRADITIONAL NAME: GROUGARRONG
TIGER — TRADITIONAL NAME: BONINBARNGEET
PETER — TRADITIONAL NAME: ARRAHMUNIJARRIMUN
JIM CROW — TRADITIONAL NAME: JALLACHNIURRIMIN

ASHES CONTINUES ...

REMEMBER WHICH TEAM YOU ARE ON, SKIPPER. WG SEEMS TO BE SUBSTITUTING IN YOUR BRAIN

IN THE FIRST EVER TEST AT LORD'S, ENGLAND WON BY AN INNINGS. THEY WERE HELPED BY BILLY MURDOCH CATCHING ONE OF HIS OWN MEN WHILE SUBSTITUTING FOR WG GRACE.

THE TEST AT THE OVAL WAS DRAWN.
BUT MURDOCH GOT THE FIRST EVER DOUBLE HUNDRED,
AND ENGLAND WICKETKEEPER ALFRED LYTTELTON
TOOK 4 WICKETS BOWLING OLD-FASHIONED LOBS
BILLY MIDWINTER WAS THE FIRST VICTIM OF LOBS IN A TEST MATCH

I SPY ANOTHER GREAT CARICATURE

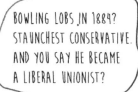

BOWLING LOBS IN 1884? STAUNCHEST CONSERVATIVE. AND YOU SAY HE BECAME A LIBERAL UNIONIST?

1884-85 - THE TOUR, A BUSINESS VENTURE OF THE SPORTING FIRM SET UP BY ARTHUR SHREWSBURY AND ALFRED SHAW, WAS FRAUGHT WITH ACCIDENTS AND BICKERING

YORKSHIRE ALLROUNDER GEORGE ULYETT FELL OFF THE BOAT AT CLARENCE, DANGEROUSLY CLOSE TO A SHARK. HE DREW HIS KNIFE TO PROTECT HIMSELF, BUT LUCKILY THE SHARK DID NOT ATTACK.

LANCASHIRE'S JOHNNY BRIGGS WAS NEARLY KILLED WHEN A HORSE ALMOST KICKED HIM OFF FITZROY FALLS. ANOTHER HORSE THREW HIM OFF HIS BACK AND HIS PIPE STEM GOT STUCK TO THE ROOF OF HIS MOUTH

MEANWHILE THE AUSTRALIAN CAMP WAS SEVERELY DIVIDED WITH SEVERAL PLAYERS DEMANDING MORE RETURNS FROM THE GATE MONEY.

HORAN

SPOFFORTH

MURDOCH

BLACKHAM

AS A RESULT, WEAK SIDES TURNED OUT TO PLAY SOME OF THE TESTS

AND TO THINK DOWN THE YEARS THEY WILL BELIEVE CRICKET WAS A GENTLEMAN'S GAME

I GUESS ONE NEEDS MONEY TO BE A GENTLEMAN

ACTUALLY OUR FRIEND HERE HAS HIT UPON A VERY IMPORTANT TRUTH

KING LEOPOLD II OF BELGIUM ESTABLISHES THE CONGO AS A PERSONAL COLONIAL POSSESSION

England win series 3-2

IN SPITE OF ALL THIS THE SERIES SAW A CLOSELY FOUGHT 3-2 RESULT IN FAVOUR OF ENGLAND.

SYDNEY PARDON

AS A WIDE POOL OF CRICKETERS WERE BEING TRIED OUT FOR AUSTRALIA, SAM MORRIS OF WEST INDIAN ORIGINS BECAME THE FIRST BLACK MAN TO PLAY TEST CRICKET

1886-87

I THOUGHT THINGS WOULD CHANGE NOW THAT AUSTRALIA HAVE GONE SCOTT-FREE.

MODERN DAY CRICKET IS DECAYING. THESE TEST MATCHES HAVE NO FUTURE.

VERY FEW PEOPLE TURNED UP TO WATCH ENGLAND DEFEAT A WEAK AUSTRALIAN SIDE 2-0 IN 1886-87.

ONE OF THE GREATEST UNCHANGING TRADITIONS OF CRICKET IS THE RANT 'CRICKET IS DECAYING'

YOU REALLY THINK PEOPLE WILL GET THE PUN ON TUP SCOTT'S NAME?

EVEN THE EMERGENCE OF THE DREADED TURNER-FERRIS COMBINATION DID NOT HELP THE AUSTRALIANS. THEY TOOK 35 WICKETS IN THE TWO TESTS AND ALMOST WON IT FOR AUSTRALIA AT MELBOURNE, BUT AN ALL-ROUND PERFORMANCE BY BILLY BARNES SEALED IT FOR ENGLAND

BARNES MISSED THE NEXT TEST AT SYDNEY BECAUSE HE HAD THROWN A PUNCH AT PERCY MCDONNELL AND HIT A WALL INSTEAD

IT WAS ACTUALLY HUGH HIDDILSTON I WAS AIMING AT

ON BEING DISMISSED IN THE SECOND INNINGS, BARNES WALKED AWAY AND THEN CAME BACK TO PAT THE WICKET WITH HIS BAT — IMPLYING THE CONDITIONS WERE NOT SUITABLE.

TODAY IT WOULD COST HIM HIS MATCH FEES AND PROBABLY GET HIM A BAN

IN 1887-88, TWO ENGLISH TEAMS ARRIVED IN AUSTRALIA, PLAYING AN ENORMOUS NUMBER OF MATCHES. ONE TEAM WAS LED BY GEORGE VERNON AND HON MARTIN BLADEN HAWKE, THE OTHER BY ARTHUR SHREWSBURY

> A PIECE OF FOLLY (THAT) WILL NEVER BE PERPETRATED AGAIN

THE AUSTRALIAN PRESS AND PUBLIC WERE INTRIGUED BY THE DIFFERENCES BETWEEN THE AMATEURS AND PROFESSIONALS. IN ADELAIDE, THE AMATEURS STAYED AT THE SOUTH AUSTRALIAN CLUB WHILE THE PROFESSIONALS AT THE PRINCE ALBERT HOTEL.

HON HAWKE

> OUR PROFESSIONALS PREFER TO BE ON THEIR OWN OFF THE FIELD RATHER THAN IN THE SAME HOTEL AS THE AMATEURS. SOME OF OUR PROFESSIONALS WOULD PREFER TO HAVE SECOND-CLASS PASSAGES ON BOARD SHIP RATHER THAN HAVING TO DRESS FOR DINNER. THIS IS NOT DIMINISHING THE PERFECT ACCORD BETWEEN THE AMATEURS AND PROFESSIONALS

> EVEN IN THOSE DAYS THE AUSTRALIANS REALISED HON HAWKE'S JUSTIFICATIONS WERE WHAT WILL BE NOW CALLED 'AMATEURISH'

HAWKE HAD TO RETURN DUE TO HIS FATHER'S DEMISE. THUS HE BECAME LORD HAWKE. THE AMATEURS AND PROFESSIONALS POOLED THEIR RESOURCES TO WIN THE ONLY TEST. GEORGE LOHMANN AND BOBBY PEEL UPSTAGED YET ANOTHER DESTRUCTIVE TURNER-FERRIS SHOW

> THIS WAS PERHAPS THE WORST EVER TEST MATCH TO BE GIVEN TEST STATUS

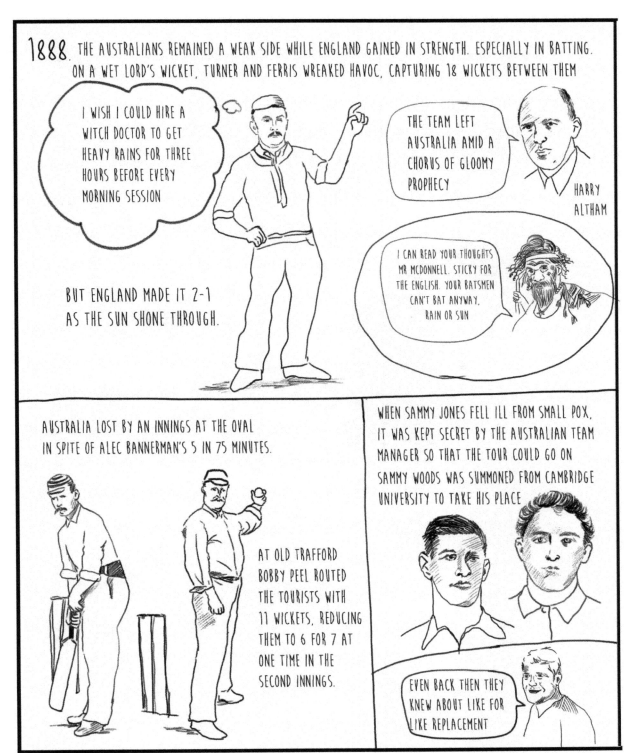

1890. THE AUSTRALIAN TOUR WAS WHAT WISDEN CALLED "A DISAPPOINTMENT."
BULLETIN CALLED IT 'A FORTUNE FOR BREWERS'
NOT LEAST OF THEIR PROBLEMS WAS KENNY BURN MISTAKENLY TAKEN AS
THE BACKUP WICKETKEEPER FOR THE SKIPPER, THE GREAT JACK BLACKHAM.
ACTUALLY, HIS BROTHER JAMES WAS A KEEPER, NOT KENNY.

STAND BEHIND THE
STUMPS, YOU ARE
THE RESERVE KEEPER.

KEN IS NOT
ABEL TO KEEP.

AM I?
MY BROTHER'S
KEEPER.

BUT THE TEST SERIES COULD HAVE BEEN 1-1
IF THE AUSTRALIANS HAD KEPT THEIR HEADS.

BARRETT, YOU CARRIED THE BAT
AT LORD'S. COULDN'T YOU DO
THE SAME WITH THE BALL HERE?

AT THE OVAL, WITH 2 WICKETS TO FALL,
BATSMEN STRANDED MID-PITCH, THE WINNING
RUNS WERE GRANTED BY OVERTHROWS.

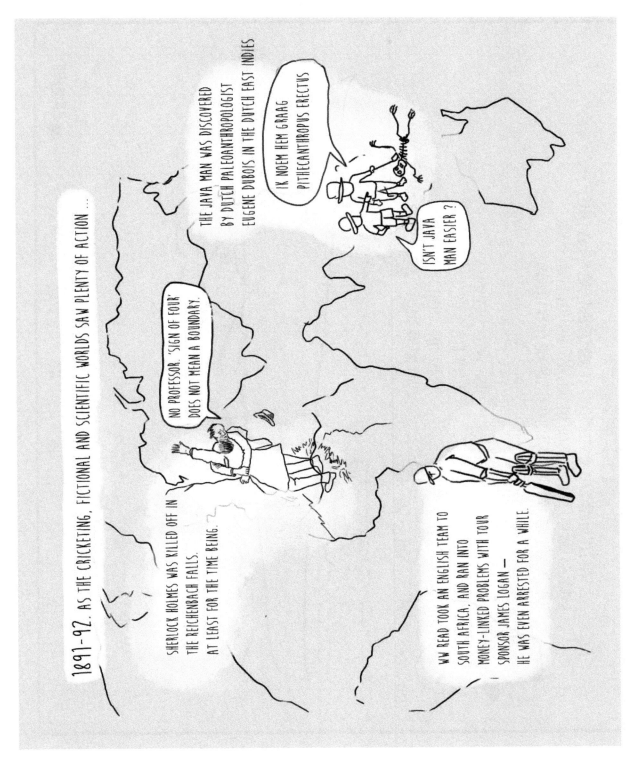

THE FOLLOWING SERIES WAS THE RESULT OF A DESPERATE CRY FOR HELP.

THE SPECULATIVE BOOM IN THE AUSTRALIAN PROPERTY MARKET OF THE 1880S HAD ENDED IN A SEVERE CRASH. IN JANUARY 1893, THE FEDERAL BANK HAD FAILED. BY MID-MAY ELEVEN COMMERCIAL BANKS HAD SUSPENDED TRADING. THE COUNTRY WAS IN THE MIDST OF A FULL-FLEDGED FINANCIAL CRISIS. THE COLLAPSE OF THE CITY OF MELBOURNE BANK HAD LEFT THE MELBOURNE CRICKET CLUB £2,336 IN DEBT. FRANK GREY SMITH, PRESIDENT OF MELBOURNE CRICKET CLUB, HAD TAKEN OUT A PERSONAL OVERDRAFT FROM NATIONAL BANK. HE HAD APPROACHED LORD SHEFFIELD WITH THE PROPOSAL OF BRINGING OVER AN ENGLAND SIDE TO RESTORE THE FINANCIAL CONDITION OF THE PREMIER AUSTRALIAN CRICKETING BODY. SHEFFIELD HAD REFUSED, BUT ANDREW STODDART HAD AGREED TO ORGANISE A TEAM TO TOUR THE COLONIES

THE RUBBER SPARKED OFF THE FRENZIED INTEREST WHICH HAS ALWAYS SINCE SURROUNDED TEST MATCHES BETWEEN ENGLAND AND AUSTRALIA.
YES, IT WAS A PATH-BREAKING SERIES IN MANY SENSES

DAVID FRITH

DREWY STODDART — STODDY- FINISHED THE TOUR AS THE MOST POPULAR ENGLISH CAPTAIN IN AUSTRALIA. ONE OF THE BEST BATSMEN OF HIS DAY, AN ENGLAND RUGBY THREE-QUARTER AND CAPTAIN, AN AUSTRALIAN RULES FOOTBALLER ... THE MOST VERSATILE SPORTSMAN OF ENGLAND. HIS TEAM CONTAINED GIANT NAMES.

BILL LOCKWOOD FAST AND INTIMIDATING

STODDY

ARCHIE MACLAREN SYMBOLISED GOLDEN AGE OF CRICKET

TOM RICHARDSON HONEST, HARD WORKING, CURLY DARK HAIR, AND WILLINGNESS TO BOWL FAST

BOBBY PEEL 'TERRIER ON RAT' WITH BATSMEN

JOHNNY BRIGGS 118 TEST WICKETS AT 18 APIECE

JACK BLACKHAM
CAPTAIN
SUPREME
AMONG
KEEPERS

SO DID THE AUSTRALIAN SIDE WITH THEIR OWN
STALWARTS, PLAYING WITH A PASSION WHICH
WOULD HAVE COMPARED FAVOURABLY WITH
CRICKETERS TODAY

GEORGE GIFFEN
WG OF
AUSTRALIA

JOE DARLING
THIS WAS THE FIRST
SERIES OF A REMARKABLE
CAREER

ERNIE JONES
MINER, STEVEDORE
AND FAST BOWLER

ALBERT TROTT WILLING, POWERFUL BATSMAN AND A BOWLER
WITH PACE, SWING, CUT, SPIN AND SHEER SURPRISE

THE FIRST TEST AT SYDNEY WAS PROBABLY THE MOST SENSATIONAL MATCH EVER PLAYED EITHER IN ENGLAND OR IN AUSTRALIA.

AUSTRALIA FIRST INNINGS — BIG HUNDREDS BY GEORGE GIFFEN AND SYD GREGORY HELPED THE HOSTS TO 586

ALBERT WARD TOP-SCORED IN BOTH THE ENGLAND INNINGS, BUT THE VISITORS HAD TO FOLLOW ON BECAUSE OF SOME SUPERB BOWLING BY GIFFEN

AT THE END OF THE FIFTH DAY, NEEDING 177 TO WIN, AUSTRALIA WERE 113 FOR 2, GIFFEN AND DARLING GOING STRONG. SOME ENGLISH PLAYERS RESORTED TO DRINK TO GET OVER THE DISAPPOINTMENT

IT RAINED LAST NIGHT.

AND BLACKHAM'S FACE BECAME LONG.

CAPTAIN STODDART HAD TO GET THE BOOZIEST OF THEM ALL, BOBBY PEEL, SOBERED FOR ACTION. HE WAS A MATCHWINNER ON WET WICKETS.

GIVE ME THE BALL, MR STODDART, AND I'LL GET T'BOOGERS OUT BEFORE LOONCH.

PEEL CAPTURED 6 AND WHEN AN INJURED BLACKHAM WAS DISMISSED IN HIS FINAL TEST, ENGLAND WON BY 10 RUNS.

ON THIS ALICE-IN-WONDERLAND DAY OF CRICKET, CRICKET-MAD AUSTRALIAN PRIME MINISTER ROBERT MENZIES CHOSE TO BE BORN.

AFTER THE FOURTH TEST THE SERIES WAS TIED 2-2, WITH SUPERB PERFORMANCES FROM EVERYONE. ESPECIALLY ALBERT TROTT, WHO SCORED 110 AND CAPTURED 8 WICKETS ON DEBUT

IN THE DECIDER AT MELBOURNE ENGLAND WERE SET A STEEP 297 TO WIN. COMING IN AT 28 FOR 2, JACK BROWN BLASTED HIS WAY TO WHAT IS STILL THE FASTEST ASHES FIFTY (28 MINUTES, 34 BALLS) AND THEN RACED TO HIS HUNDRED IN 95 MINUTES. ENGLAND WON BY 6 WICKETS AND HENCE TOOK THE SERIES

1882–83 Eng 2 Aus 1 (Additional Test won by Aus)
1884   Eng 1 Aus 0
1884–85 Eng 3 Aus 2
1886   Eng 3 Aus 0
1886–87 Eng 2 Aus 0
1887–88 Eng 1 Aus 0
1888   Eng 2 Aus 1
1890   Eng 2 Aus 0
1891–92   Aus 2 Eng 1
1893   Eng 1 Aus 0
1894–95 Eng 3 Aus 2

Cumulative Ashes Head to Head
Tests - Eng 21 Aus 8
Series - Eng 10 Aus 1

ENG   AUS

THAT WAS THE FIRST REALLY BIG TEST SERIES. BY THIS TIME TEST MATCHES WERE BEING TAKEN VERY SERIOUSLY INDEED.

IT WAS DURING THESE REPORTS OF THE 1894-95 SERIES THAT PALL MALL GAZETTE SPELT 'TEST' WITH A CAPITAL 'T' FOR THE FIRST TIME IN CRICKET HISTORY. FROM THAT EPOCHAL DAY 'test cricket' BECAME 'Test cricket'.

THESE WERE THE VERY EARLY YEARS, RIGHT? THE PRISTINE PERIOD. AND YOU ARE TELLING ME CRICKET WAS PLAYED FOR FINANCIAL REASONS AND THERE WAS ALWAYS SO MUCH BICKERING ABOUT MONEY? WG GRACE WAS SO CHURLISH DURING THE 1891-92 TOUR AND ALL THAT?

CRICKET AND FINANCES HAVE ALWAYS BEEN LINKED. IT WAS NEVER OTHERWISE. AND CRICKETERS WERE NEVER SAINTS AS THEY ARE OFTEN VENERATED AS.

AS WE HAVE EXPLAINED, THIS SERIES WAS VERY IMPORTANT IN REMEDIATING THE FINANCIAL SITUATION OF MELBOURNE CRICKET CLUB

WHETHER IT WAS PLAYED FOR MONEY OR NOT, THE LAST ONE WAS A CRACKING SERIES. EVEN THE BIRTH OF THE ASHES WAS ENGINEERED BY WG GRACE'S GAMESMANSHIP, RUNNING YOUNG SAMMY JONES OUT. BUT ALL THAT MATTERS IS THAT IT RESULTED IN A FANTASTIC TEST MATCH.

1896 - 1912

TEST CRICKET GETS STANDARDISED

THE YEARS THAT FOLLOWED, LEADING UP TO THE FIRST WORLD WAR, SAW THE EMERGENCE OF SEVERAL SUPREME GREATS OF THE GAME.

WHILE WG GRACE BOWED OUT OF THE FRAY IN 1899, THE CRICKET WORLD HAILED NEW HEROES SUCH AS KS RANJITSINHJI, VICTOR TRUMPER, CLEM HILL, WILFRED RHODES, GEORGE HIRST, SF BARNES, MONTY NOBLE, WARWICK ARMSTRONG, JACK HOBBS AND MANY OTHERS.

THIS LED TO SOME THRILLING CONTESTS AND CLOSELY-FOUGHT SERIES. THE CRICKET LANDSCAPE WAS FURTHER ENRICHED BY THE DEVELOPMENT OF SOUTH AFRICA AS A SERIOUS THIRD COMPETITIVE DIMENSION. ALL THIS LED TO THE EXPERIMENTAL TRIANGULAR TEST SERIES OF 1912.

THIS ERA ALSO SAW EXCITING INNOVATIONS COMING INTO CRICKET, SUCH AS THE GOOGLY AND INCREASING SWING BOWLING. ON THE OTHER HAND, THE PERIOD WAS INTERRUPTED BY THE BOER WAR, WHICH THEN RANKED AS THE BLOODIEST EVER IN THE HISTORY OF MANKIND. IT WAS TO BE SOON SUPERSEDED BY THE GREAT WAR WHICH STOPPED TEST CRICKET — AND NORMAL LIFE — FOR FIVE YEARS.

IF WE DON'T HAVE ANY CUT OFF, ALBERT TROTT IS THE ONLY ONE WHO AVERAGES MORE THAN BRADMAN IN THE ASHES 205 RUNS AT 102.50 AND 9 WICKETS AT 21.33 IN 3 TESTS AND HE WAS NOT TAKEN ON THE 1896 TOUR ... IN AN AUSTRALIAN SIDE LED BY HIS BROTHER HARRY TROTT

HE WENT TO ENGLAND ON HIS OWN, SETTLED THERE AND LATER PLAYED FOR MIDDLESEX. DOWN THE LINE HE ALSO REPRESENTED ENGLAND AGAINST SOUTH AFRICA.

ISN'T HE THE GUY WHO BLASTED THE SIXER OVER THE LORD'S PAVILION. WHERE IS HIS MOUSTACHE?

HE WAS A SLIP OF A LAD ONCE.

WHEN THE AUSTRALIANS ARRIVED IN 1899, TROTT TURNED UP FOR MIDDLESEX AGAINST THEM AND HIT MONTY NOBLE OVER THE PAVILION OF LORD'S

The Ashes

HOWEVER, AUSTRALIA WON A TENSE FINISH EVEN AS SKIPPER HARRY TROTT RODE A CAB AROUND THE GROUND TO KEEP FROM SUCCUMBING TO TENSION

HE TAKES HIS NAME TROTT TOO LITERALLY

TROTT WAS NOT THE ONLY ONE ASSOCIATED WITH THE GAME ABSENT FROM THE GROUND. CARDUS DID NOT WATCH THE GAME, BUT WROTE OF TOM RICHARDSON

"THE PLAYERS RAN OFF THE FIELD —— ALL OF THEM, SAVE RICHARDSON. HE STOOD AT THE BOWLING CREASE, DAZED. COULD THE MATCH HAVE BEEN LOST? HIS SPIRIT PROTESTED. COULD IT BE THAT THE GODS HAD LOOKED ON AND PERMITTED SO MUCH PAINFUL STRIVING TO GO BY UNREWARDED? HIS BODY STILL SHOOK FROM THE VIOLENT MOTION. HE STOOD THERE LIKE SOME FINE ANIMAL BAFFLED AT THE USELESSNESS OF GREAT STRENGTH AND EFFORT IN THIS WORLD ...
A COMPANION LED HIM TO THE PAVILION AND THERE HE FELL WEARILY TO A SEAT."

ACTUAL EYEWITNESSES, THOUGH, HAD A DIFFERENT VERSION

AS HJ HENLEY SAID, AFTER THE WINNING HIT TOM LEGGED IT TO THE PAVILION LIKE A STAG AND GOT DOWN TWO PINTS BEFORE ANYONE ELSE.... I CAN SEE TWO AUSTRALIANS AND ELEVEN ENGLISHMEN LEGGING IT TO THE PAVILION WITH THE TALL FIGURE OF TOM RICHARDSON LEADING BY MANY YARDS...

TOM AGATE

STODDY'S SAD SWANSONG

THE 1897-98 TOUR OF STODDART'S MEN STARTED TRAGICALLY. THE HEROIC CAPTAIN OF 1894-95 RECEIVED THE NEWS OF HIS MOTHER'S DEATH AND WENT INTO SEVERE DEPRESSION.

ARCHIE MACLAREN TOOK OVER THE CAPTAINCY.

HE AND RANJI STRUCK CENTURIES IN THE FIRST TEST. ENGLAND WON CONVINCINGLY.

THEREAFTER THE TOUR WENT HORRIBLY FOR ENGLAND. GREAT NEW HEROES FOR AUSTRALIA EMERGED AS ENGLAND FOUND ALL SORTS OF PROBLEMS IN THEIR CRICKET.

CLEM HILL

MONTY NOBLE

HUGH TRUMBLE

HILL AND NOBLE SHOULDN'T BE PLAYING WITH MEN. IT IS STILL THE 1800S ANDTHEY DON'T HAVE MOUSTACHES. BUT THEN THERE'S TRUMBLE...

HE CLAIMS TO BE HILL, BUT IS MAKING A MOUNTAIN OF RUNS. AND THERE IS NOTHING NOBLE ABOUT SWERVING BALLS IN THAT WAY.

58 FOR SIX. CUT OUT ALL THIS RUBBISH, YOU LEAVE THE BALL OUTSIDE THE OFF-STUMP ALONE, DO YOU HEAR ME?

HUGHIE TRUMBLE MADE EVERY RUN I GOT THAT DAY

STODDY RETURNED FOR THE THIRD AND FOURTH TESTS BUT HE WAS IN POOR FORM AND SPIRITS.

EVEN WHEN AUSTRALIA WERE 6/58 AT MELBOURNE, HILL AND TRUMBLE ADDED 165 AS HILL HIT 188

ENGLAND WERE SOON COMPLAINING ABOUT UMPIRING DECISIONS AS WELL

EVEN BUSHFIRES AND FLIES WORKED AGAINST THE ENGLISHMEN

MACLAREN WAS BOWLED WHEN A FLY SUPPOSEDLY FLEW INTO HIS EYE.

WITH THE FEDERATION APPROACHING, THE AUSTRALIAN TEAM AND CROWDS DISPLAYED EVERY BIT OF NATIONALISM. THIS FOUND EXPRESSION IN COMPETITIVENESS ON THE FIELD AND BARRACKING FROM THE CROWDS

ENGLAND LOST 4-1 AS STODDART HARDLY MADE ANY IMPACT IN THE FINAL TESTS OF HIS CAREER. HE WAS DEPRESSED ALL THROUGH, PLAGUED BY THE HEAT AND INSECT BITES. EVEN HIS POPULARITY AMONG LADIES WAS NOT A SOLACE.

1899 WG SIGNS OFF

THE SERIES ENDED 1-0 IN FAVOUR OF AUSTRALIA WITH FOUR DRAWS. THE FIRST TEST AT NOTTINGHAM WITNESSED THE FINAL SIGHT OF WG IN AN ENGLAND SIDE.

NOW REMEMBER CHARLES, I AM NOT A SPRINTER LIKE YOU.

GRACE STEPPED DOWN WITH UNCHARACTERISTIC TACT

THERE'S CHARLES. NOW BEFORE YOU SIT DOWN, DO YOU THINK MACLAREN SHOULD PLAY IN THE NEXT TEST?

YES

THAT SETTLES IT. HE PLAYS IN MY PLACE.

VOLUNTEERS RUSHED TO THE BATTLEFIELDS, FROM BOTH ENGLAND AND AUSTRALIA THAT INCLUDED CRICKETERS.

FRANK MILLIGAN, WHO PLAYED TWO TESTS AGAINST SOUTH AFRICA IN 1899, DIED IN THE CAMPAIGN TO FREE MAFEKING

JJ FERRIS OF THE DEADLY TURNER-FERRIS DUO ALSO FOUGHT IN THE BOER WAR. HE DIED IN DURBAN WHILE STATIONED THERE. MAX BONNELL HAS ESTABLISHED THAT HE DIED OF SEIZURE... WHICH HINTS AT A STROKE OR POISONING (PERHAPS SELF-POISONING)

AT THE SAME TIME, IN JANUARY 1901 AUSTRALIA BECAME A FEDERATION

COUNTY EXPERIENCE? HE'S THE GREATEST BOWLER IN THE WORLD, THAT'S GOOD ENOUGH.

IT WAS TO THIS NEWLY FEDERATED AUSTRALIA THAT ARCHIE MACLAREN TOOK HIS TEAM. AMONGST HIS SELECTIONS WAS SF BARNES

BARNES AND NOBLE

BARNES BOWLED ENGLAND TO WIN IN THE FIRST TEST AND TOOK 13 WICKETS IN THE NEXT. BUT IN THE SECOND TEST, MONTY NOBLE ALSO CAPTURED 13 WICKETS CLINCHING VICTORY FOR AUSTRALIA.

THE TWO OF THEM TOGETHER GAVE SOMEONE AN IDEA FOR THE NAME OF A BOOKSTORE.

BARNES TWISTED HIS ANKLE IN THE THIRD TEST AND AFTER THAT AUSTRALIA RAN AWAY WITH THE SERIES.

OH DRAT! NOT AGAIN.

IN HOME ASHES TESTS, HILL HIT ONLY TWO 100S, BUT WAS OUT BETWEEN 96 AND 99 5 TIMES. THIS INCLUDED 99, 98, 97 IN 3 CONSECUTIVE INNINGS IN THIS SERIES

WITH HUGH TRUMBLE'S 28 WICKETS ALONGSIDE NOBLE'S 32, AUSTRALIA WON THE SERIES 4-1.

NEVER MIND, CLEM. 100 YEARS FROM NOW YOU'LL BE A HERO OF THE TEAM VS INDIVIDUAL CULT.

I'LL BE BACK

HE WOULD. IN 10 MORE TESTS IN AUSTRALIA, BARNES WOULD CAPTURE 54 WICKETS.

EVEN IN COPPERPLATE THAT IS MY LINE

The Ashes

68

CHASING 124 TO WIN, ENGLAND COLLAPSED FROM 92 FOR 3 TO 120 ALL OUT, AIDED BY AN AMAZING CATCH BY HILL. UNFORTUNATE TATE WAS THE LAST WICKET TO FALL.

YOU CAN MAKE FUN OF ME NOW, BUT I HAVE A BOY WHO WILL SET IT RIGHT. MAURICE IS HIS NAME.

AT THE OVAL, TRUMBLE'S 8 WICKETS AND 64 NOT OUT MEANT ENGLAND AVOIDED FOLLOW ON BY JUST 9 RUNS

I THOUGHT ALL THE CORONATION PARTIES WOULD SLOW THE KANGAROOS DOWN.

ARCHIE MACLAREN

ENGLAND WERE 48 FOR 5 CHASING 263 TO WIN WHEN GILBERT JESSOP PLAYED ONE OF THE MOST INCREDIBLE INNINGS EVER. 104 IN 77 MINUTES.

HIRST AND RHODES GOT THE FINAL 15 RUNS FOR THE LAST WICKET, AND ENGLAND SQUEEZED HOME BY 1 WICKET.

NO, WE DID NOT SAY 'LET'S GET THEM IN SINGLES'. WE DID NOT CALL THEM SINGLES THEN. BESIDES, WE COULD HAVE GOT A TWO.

WILFRED RHODES

DAVID FRITH

AFTER FOUR CONSECUTIVE SERIES DEFEATS, IT WAS FELT THAT THE HONOUR OF ENGLISH CRICKET WAS NOW SERIOUSLY AT STAKE. VERY PROPERLY THE MCC SET OUT TO VINDICATE IT BY UNDERTAKING IN 1903-04, FOR THE FIRST TIME, TO SEND OUT A TEAM UNDER THEIR DIRECT AUSPICES.

HARRY ALTHAM

PLUM WARNER WAS NOT THE FIRST CHOICE AS CAPTAIN. HE GOT THE JOB AFTER JACKSON AND FRY SAID 'NO' DUE TO VARIOUS REASONS.

EW SWANTON

IN FACT, THE FIRST MCC TOUR WOULD HAVE BEEN SOONER IF NOT FOR THE BOER WAR

WARNER'S APPOINTMENT LED TO CONTROVERSY AND SOME ANGRY WORDS EXCHANGED WITH MACLAREN. HOWEVER, IN HIS BOOK ON THE TOUR, WARNER CAREFULLY AVOIDED ANY MENTION OF THIS — SETTING TONE FOR HIS APPROACH FOR THE NEXT HALF-CENTURY

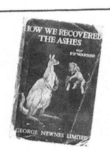

ON *SS ORONTES* WARNER CAME ACROSS JAMES WELLDON, THE CANON OF WESTMINSTER, THE FORMER BISHOP OF CALCUTTA

BISHOP, IS IT CHRISTIAN TO PRAY TO BEAT AUSTRALIA?

ANYTHING THAT TENDS TO THE PRESTIGE OF ENGLAND IS WORTH PRAYING FOR. AFTER SAYING YOUR PRAYERS, BE A BIT DISCREET WITH THE LADIES ON BOARD.

THE BISHOP STOOD UMPIRE AS A GROUP OF LADIES DEFEATED THE ENGLISH CRICKETERS AT A GAME OF DECK CRICKET

NO GEORGE, NOW'S NOT THE TIME. MY BACK IS KILLING ME, AND THERE'S A CLERGYMAN IN THE CROWD.

1905. AS JACKSON REPLACED MACLAREN AS REGULAR CAPTAIN OF ENGLAND, MACLAREN'S BAT ROARED AND BOSANQUET BAMBOOZLED THEM YET AGAIN AT TRENT BRIDGE.

TRUMPER, HAVING HURT HIS BACK, WAS CARRIED TO THE GATE BY TEAMMATES, BUT COULD NOT WALK TO THE CREASE.

THANKS TO GEORGE BELDAM I HAVE SOME READY REFERENCE PHOTOGRAPHS TO WORK ON. ELSE IT WOULD HAVE BEEN BEDLAM.

AT OLD TRAFFORD, JACKSON SCORED A HUNDRED AS ENGLAND MADE THE SERIES 2-0. THE REST OF THE TESTS WERE DRAWN. AUSTRALIANS, PLAGUED WITH PROBLEMS OF CASH-CONTROL BETWEEN PLAYERS AND ADMINISTRATORS, DID NOT PERFORM WELL.

TRUMPER, HILL, DARLING, GREGORY WERE ALL OUT OF FORM. THE BOWLING SUFFERED FROM THE RECENT RETIREMENT OF TRUMBLE. TIBBY COTTER BOWLED FAST AND AGGRESSIVELY, AND ARMSTRONG PITCHED HIS LEG-BREAKS NEGATIVELY, USING LEG THEORY.

HARRY ALTHAM

WE CAN SETTLE IT THAT WAY, BUT IN THAT CASE HIRST WILL BE OUR MAN.

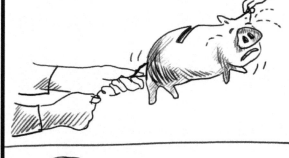

IT WAS JACKSON'S YEAR

FRUSTRATED BY JACKSON WINNING THE TOSS EVERY TIME, IN THE TOUR MATCH AT SCARBOROUGH, DARLING CHALLENGED HIM TO A WRESTLING MATCH INSTEAD OF A FLIP OF THE COIN.

ALAN GIBSON

WHAT DOES HE THINK I AM? A CHANGE BOWLER?

1911-12   AS THE DESIGNATED CAPTAIN PLUM WARNER FELL ILL, THE RESPONSIBILITY OF LEADING THE TEAM FELL ON THE SHOULDERS OF JWHT DOUGLAS.

IN THE FIRST TEST, DOUGLAS TOOK THE NEW BALL WITH FRANK FOSTER. THIS LEFT SF BARNES FUMING. THE ACE BOWLER DID NOT PERFORM AND ENGLAND LOST THE TEST.

BARNES BOWLS FIRST. ALWAYS. ELSE JOHNNY WONT BE A HIT TODAY OR ANY DAY.

IT FELL UPON WARNER TO PERSUADE DOUGLAS TO DESIST FROM SUCH ILL-ADVISED TACTICS.

IN THE SECOND TEST BETTER SENSES PREVAILED. BARNES STARTED WITH A FAMOUS OPENING SPELL. AFTER THAT BARNES AND FOSTER RAN THROUGH THE AUSTRALIANS AGAIN AND AGAIN. RHODES, IN HIS NEW ROLE AS AN OPENING BATSMAN, PROVED A PERFECT FOIL FOR THE GREAT JACK HOBBS. ENGLAND WON THE SERIES 4-1

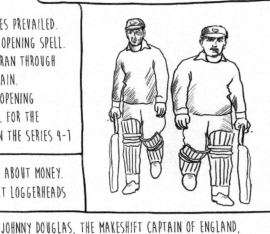

AT THE SAME TIME, THE AUSTRALIANS GOT INTO A BITTER CONFLICT ABOUT MONEY. TRUMPER, HILL, ARMSTRONG, CARTER, COTTER AND RANSFORD WAS AT LOGGERHEADS AGAINST THE BOARD. IT WAS KNOWN AS THE BIG SIX FACEOFF.

OH WHAT A SHAME. IN MY TIME, BIG SIX MEANT JESSOPUS OR BONNOR.

BILLY MURDOCH 1854 - 1911

JOHNNY DOUGLAS, THE MAKESHIFT CAPTAIN OF ENGLAND, WAS AN OLYMPIC BOXING GOLD MEDALIST. BUT ON THIS TOUR, IT WAS THE AUSTRALIAN CAPTAIN CLEM HILL WHO THREW THE PUNCHES. AT A SELECTION COMMITTEE MEETING, FED UP WITH PETER MCALLISTER, A MEDIOCRE CRICKETER AND A YES-BOARD STOOGE, HILL ENDED UP PUNCHING HIM IN THE FACE

HOW HARD HE PUNCHED IS DISPUTED. WHATEVER THE FORCE A FIGHT ENSUED FOR PERHAPS AS LONG AS TWENTY MINUTES. HILL HAD TO BE RESTRAINED FROM PUSHING MCALISTER THROUGH THE THIRD-FLOOR WINDOW

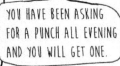

YOU HAVE BEEN ASKING FOR A PUNCH ALL EVENING AND YOU WILL GET ONE.

THE BIG SIX

FRANK FOSTER AND SF BARNES COMBINED INTO ONE OF THE MOST LETHAL COMBINATIONS

FOSTER CAPTURED 32 WICKETS IN THE SERIES, BARNES 34

BARNES ENDED HIS CAREER WITH 189 WICKETS IN 27 TESTS AT 16.43

A THOROUGH PROFESSIONAL, HE PLAYED MORE LANCASHIRE LEAGUE THAN FIRST-CLASS CRICKET

HE WAS STILL TAKING WICKETS BY THE HEAP IN HIS LATE 50S

IF HE HAD BEEN SUPPORTED A BIT MORE BY MCC, HE WOULD HAVE ENDED UP WITH MANY, MANY MORE TEST WICKETS

HIS GENIUS CAN PROBABLY BE DECONSTRUCTED FROM A PIECE OF ADVICE HE GAVE HUGH TAYFIELD. 'DON'T TAKE ANY NOTICE OF ANYTHING ANYBODY EVER TELLS YOU'

SINCE THEY ARE NOT SAYING ANYTHING ABOUT FOSTER, LET ME TELL YOU — HE WILL RETURN IN THE STORY

THREE WAY CRICKET   THE 1912 ASHES WAS MERGED WITH THE TRIANGULAR TEST TOURNAMENT FEATURING ENGLAND, AUSTRALIA AND SOUTH AFRICA.

The Times Dispatch

TITANIC DISASTER

Sunk after collision with iceberg

SUFFRAGIST OUTRAGES

BRITAIN AND GERMANY IN BATTLESHIP RACE

WETTEST SUMMER IN THE OFFING

TRIANGULAR TEST SERIES

CONAN DOYLE CREATES NEW CHARACTER IN THE LOST WORLD

AUSTRALIAN BIG SIX STANDOFF

IT IS 31.11269837220809

THAT IS ALL VERY WELL, PYTHAGORAS. BUT COULDN'T YOU PICK A NAME SIMPLER THAN HYPOTENUSE

1896   Eng 2 Aus 1
1897-98 Aus 4 Eng 1
1899   Aus 1 Eng 0
1901-02 Aus 4 Eng 1
1902   Aus 2 Eng 1
1903-04 Eng 3 Aus 2
1905   Eng 2 Aus 0
1907-08 Aus 4 Eng 1
1909   Aus 2 Eng 1
1911-12 Eng 4 Aus 1
1912   Eng 1 Aus 0 (Triangular Test Series)

Cumulative Ashes Head to Head
Tests- Eng 38 Aus 29
Series - Eng 15 Aus 7

ENG   AUS

By this time international cricket was a more organised sport.

With the Olympics and football association becoming more professionally organised, most of the global sports were being run more methodically.

Jessop's match to the 1907-08 series. It was always a fascinating game and it remains so. That is all this is about.

The umpire being called a cheat to his face. A captain punching a selector. I can't believe it!

Things that would earn you a serious ban in the current day. Don't forget doctoring the pitches and the big six dispute. If anything, cricket is much more antiseptic today.

International sportsmen are tremendously talented individuals who play to win, and almost always to make money. They have always been like any other normal person, apart from being exceptionally good at what they do. So, is there any reason to believe that once upon a time they were saints and they suddenly became sinners?

The ICC regulations today keep a lot of these things in check. It had never been a gentleman's game and never will be. But, the regulations are stricter now.

1914-1918 . THE GREATER GAME

AS THE ACTION SHIFTED TO THE ARENA OF THE GREATER GAME, TEST CRICKET WAS PAUSED.
HUNDREDS OF CRICKETERS VOLUNTEERED THEIR SERVICES, AND MANY WERE KILLED IN ACTION.
275 FIRST-CLASS CRICKETERS PERISHED IN BATTLE, WHICH INCLUDED 12 TEST CRICKETERS.
OF THESE 3 PLAYED IN THE ASHES TESTS AS WELL.

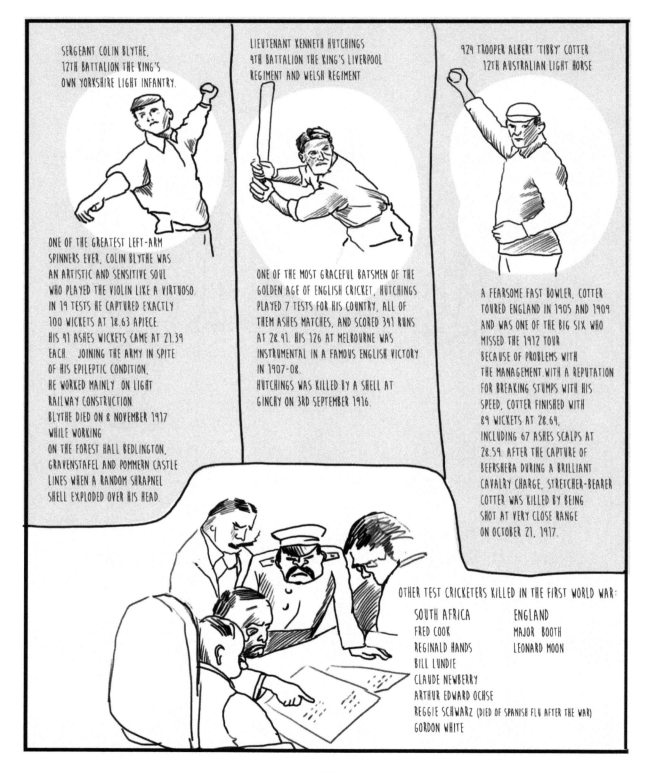

SERGEANT COLIN BLYTHE,
12TH BATTALION THE KING'S
OWN YORKSHIRE LIGHT INFANTRY.

ONE OF THE GREATEST LEFT-ARM
SPINNERS EVER, COLIN BLYTHE WAS
AN ARTISTIC AND SENSITIVE SOUL
WHO PLAYED THE VIOLIN LIKE A VIRTUOSO.
IN 19 TESTS HE CAPTURED EXACTLY
100 WICKETS AT 18.63 APIECE.
HIS 41 ASHES WICKETS CAME AT 21.39
EACH. JOINING THE ARMY IN SPITE
OF HIS EPILEPTIC CONDITION,
HE WORKED MAINLY ON LIGHT
RAILWAY CONSTRUCTION.
BLYTHE DIED ON 8 NOVEMBER 1917
WHILE WORKING
ON THE FOREST HALL BEDLINGTON,
GRAVENSTAFEL AND POMMERN CASTLE
LINES WHEN A RANDOM SHRAPNEL
SHELL EXPLODED OVER HIS HEAD.

LIEUTENANT KENNETH HUTCHINGS
4TH BATTALION THE KING'S LIVERPOOL
REGIMENT AND WELSH REGIMENT

ONE OF THE MOST GRACEFUL BATSMEN OF THE
GOLDEN AGE OF ENGLISH CRICKET, HUTCHINGS
PLAYED 7 TESTS FOR HIS COUNTRY, ALL OF
THEM ASHES MATCHES, AND SCORED 341 RUNS
AT 28.41. HIS 126 AT MELBOURNE WAS
INSTRUMENTAL IN A FAMOUS ENGLISH VICTORY
IN 1907-08.
HUTCHINGS WAS KILLED BY A SHELL AT
GINCHY ON 3RD SEPTEMBER 1916.

924 TROOPER ALBERT 'TIBBY' COTTER
12TH AUSTRALIAN LIGHT HORSE

A FEARSOME FAST BOWLER, COTTER
TOURED ENGLAND IN 1905 AND 1909
AND WAS ONE OF THE BIG SIX WHO
MISSED THE 1912 TOUR
BECAUSE OF PROBLEMS WITH
THE MANAGEMENT. WITH A REPUTATION
FOR BREAKING STUMPS WITH HIS
SPEED, COTTER FINISHED WITH
89 WICKETS AT 28.64,
INCLUDING 67 ASHES SCALPS AT
28.59. AFTER THE CAPTURE OF
BEERSHEBA DURING A BRILLIANT
CAVALRY CHARGE, STRETCHER-BEARER
COTTER WAS KILLED BY BEING
SHOT AT VERY CLOSE RANGE
ON OCTOBER 21, 1917.

OTHER TEST CRICKETERS KILLED IN THE FIRST WORLD WAR:

SOUTH AFRICA	ENGLAND
FRED COOK	MAJOR BOOTH
REGINALD HANDS	LEONARD MOON
BILL LUNDIE	
CLAUDE NEWBERRY	
ARTHUR EDWARD OCHSE	
REGGIE SCHWARZ (DIED OF SPANISH FLU AFTER THE WAR)	
GORDON WHITE	

1920 -1928-29

LIMPING BACK TO NORMALCY

TEST CRICKET TOOK OFF SLOWLY AFTER THE MAYHEM.
AS NORMALCY LIMPED BACK TO ENGLAND,
THE CRICKET OF THE WAR-WEARY LAND STUTTERED AND STUMBLED FOR A WHILE.

IN THE MEANTIME, THE AGGRESSIVE AUSTRALIANS WERE ALL BRACED FOR BATTLE.
AS A RESULT, WHEN JOHNNY DOUGLAS'S TEAM VISITED IN 1920-21,
THEY WERE HANDED THE FIRST EVER 5-0 WHITEWASH IN THE HISTORY OF THE RIVALRY.
WHEN THE AUSTRALIANS, UNDER THEIR FORMIDABLE CAPTAIN WARWICK ARMSTRONG,
RETURNED THE VISIT, THEY WON EVERYTHING IN ENGLAND ...
WELL ALMOST EVERYTHING BEFORE BEING STOPPED BY AN OLD HAND.

THE IMBALANCE OF POWER REMAINED QUITE STRIKING UNTIL 1926
WHEN ENGLAND REGAINED THE ASHES TO EVERYONE'S
SURPRISE AND MUCH WIDE-SPREAD EUPHORIA.

OH, I WILL MISS DRAWING ALL THOSE BUSHY BEARDS AND MAGNIFICENT MOUSTACHES OF THE GOLDEN AGE OF CRICKET

IN AUSTRALIA, THE ENGLISH SIDE SUFFERED THE FIRST 5-0 DEFEAT.
NO ONE EXCEPT JACK HOBBS MANAGED TO STAND UP TO THE AUSTRALIAN BOWLING. BUT BY THE END OF THE
TOUR, HE HAD PICKED UP A NASTY INJURY. ON THE OTHER HAND, THE POWERFUL AUSTRALIAN BATTING
PLUNDERED TRUCKLOADS OF RUNS. JACK GREGORY IN PARTICULAR WAS MENACING BOTH WITH BAT AND BALL.

NIP PELLEW
319 (53.16)

ARTHUR MAILEY
36 WKTS (26.27)

HERBIE
COLLINS
557 (61.88)

WARWICK
ARMSTRONG
464 (
77.33) .
9 (22.66)

CHARLES KELLEWAY
330 (47.14), 15 (21.00)

JACK GREGORY
442 (73.66), 23 (24.17)

W W ARMSTRONG

JACK HOBBS
505 (50.50)

THE RAMPAGE CONTINUED WHEN AUSTRALIA TOURED IN 1921.

ARMSTRONG RUTHLESSLY UNLEASHED THE PACE OF GREGORY AND TED MCDONALD WHO CAPTURED 46 WICKETS BETWEEN THEM. THE ABSENCE OF INJURED HOBBS DID NOT REALLY HELP ENGLAND

BARDSLEY

MACARTNEY

BATTING HEROES, TOO, CONTINUED TO EMERGE FOR AUSTRALIA.

IT WAS NOW MORE THAN EVER
THAT CRICKET WAS GIVEN
THE AURA OF BEING 'BEYOND A GAME',
A 'GENTLEMAN'S ENDEAVOUR',
BEING 'ALL ABOUT FAIR-PLAY AND MANLINESS,
THE EPITOME OF BRITISHNESS'.
THE LURE OF 'AMATEUR ETHOS' AND
'GENTLEMAN CRICKETER' WAS
VOICED BY LORD HAWKE IN 1924

PRAY GOD, NO PROFESSIONAL
SHALL EVER CAPTAIN ENGLAND

1924-25 WAS A GREAT TRIUMPH OF THE NEWLY-FORMED OPENING DUO OF ENGLAND.

JACK HOBBS (573 RUNS 63.66) AND HERBERT SUTCLIFFE (734 RUNS 81.55) ADDED 868 RUNS IN 9 INNINGS.

BUT THE REST OF THE BATTING HARDLY GAVE THEM ANY SUPPORT.

GET ONE OF THEM, MATE. IT IS 'WELL BEGUN FULL DONE' IN THIS CASE

HOBBS AND SUTCLIFFE SHARED 11 CENTURY PARTNERSHIPS IN THE ASHES. NO ONE ELSE SHARED MORE THAN 5.
OF COURSE, IN KEEPING WITH THE HAWKE DICTUM, NEITHER OF THEM LED ENGLAND

HOWEVER, SUPPOSEDLY GILLIGAN LEFT MORE THAN JUST SPORTING BONHOMIE AND DISCARDED BALLS IN HIS WAKE.

WHAT HAVE WE HERE? FASCIST ENROLMENT FORMS, INTERNAL MEMORANDA AND PROPAGANDA. CURIOUS, ALL THESE SEEM TO BE PRINTED IN LONDON. GOOD THAT THE BRITISH SS WARNED US ABOUT GILLIGAN.

ACCORDING TO HISTORIAN ANDREW MOORE OF WESTERN SYDNEY UNIVERSITY: "IT SEEMS LIKELY THAT ARTHUR GILLIGAN FOLLOWED THE ADVICE ISSUED BY THE FASCISTS RECRUITING AND PROPAGANDA DEPARTMENT. THIS WAS TO 'TALK ABOUT THE MOVEMENT TO EVERYONE YOU MEET' AND 'ALWAYS CARRY AT LEAST ONE ENROLMENT FORM AND ONE OF EACH OF THE OTHER PAMPHLETS WITH YOU WHEREVER YOU GO'. THE LITERATURE OF THE FASCISTS PROBABLY ARRIVED IN THE LUGGAGE THAT GILLIGAN AND MANAGER FREDERICK TOONE BROUGHT TO AUSTRALIA IN 1924"

ROBERT BROOKE, THE WARWICKSHIRE CRICKET HISTORIAN, ADDS THAT GILLIGAN SPENT HIS SPARE TIME EXTOLLING THE VIRTUES OF BENITO MUSSOLINI'S FASCISM.

ENGLAND WERE SAVED BY HOBBS AND SUTCLIFFE AT LEEDS. AT OLD TRAFFORD, CARR WAS STRUCK BY TONSILLITIS AND HOBBS LED THE SIDE FOR THE REST OF THE TEST MATCH.

LEAD ON, JACK.

YOU'RE DOING ME A GREAT HONOUR, BUT THERE'S MR STEVENS IN THE SIDE.

BUT PLUM, STEVENS IS THE AMATEUR!

GREVILLE STEVENS WAS A 25-YEAR-OLD WHO WAS PLAYING HIS SECOND TEST

JACK, WORDS LIKE THAT WILL MAKE EVEN ME SWEAR, AND I AM A SUPERCILIOUS APOLOGIST OF TRADITION.

AND HENCE, WARNER CHANGED HIS STANCE ... NOT FOR THE LAST TIME IN OUR CHRONICLES. AT THE OVAL, THE POPULAR PERCY CHAPMAN WAS NAMED SKIPPER.

RETURNING TO THE SIDE WAS WILFRED RHODES, 48, AND, AFTER A GAP OF TWO TESTS, HAROLD LARWOOD, 21.

AFTER SCORES OF 280 AND 302, ENGLAND HAD JUST WIPED OFF THE DEFICIT BY THE END OF THE THIRD DAY. BUT THEN THERE WAS HEAVY RAIN THROUGH THE NIGHT. NO ONE EXPECTED THE ENGLISH BATSMEN TO SURVIVE MORE THAN AN HOUR ON A GLUEPOT.

VITTORIO DE SICA MUST HAVE GOT THE IDEA OF YESTERDAY, TODAY AND TOMORROW AFTER SEEING THOSE THREE TOGETHER ...

HE WAS ITALIAN. THE MOST HE COULD DO WAS PROBABLY WONDER WHY THE UMPIRES WERE NOT RUNNING UP AND DOWN THE BOUNDARY LINE.

HOBBS WAS 43 PLAYING HIS 48TH TEST, SUTCLIFFE 31 IN HIS 15TH, CHAPMAN 25 AND IN HIS 10TH. CHAPMAN WAS THE AMATEUR CAPTAIN

BUT IN THE MORNING, HOBBS (100) AND SUTCLIFFE (161) PRODUCED THE MOST MAGNIFICENT DISPLAY ON A WET WICKET. ENGLAND SET A TARGET OF 415.

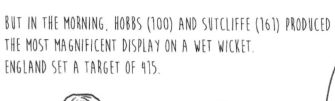

JOHN ARLOTT

IT WAS WORTH COMING ALL THE WAY FROM BASINGSTOKE FOR THIS. I WAS JUST 12 AT THAT TIME.

RHODES AND LARWOOD, LOOKING VERY MUCH LIKE A FATHER-SON DUO, PROCEEDED TO BOWL AUSTRALIA OUT FOR 125.

ONE OF THE MOST MAGNIFICENT SCENES I HAVE EVER TAKEN PART IN.

THUS ENGLAND WON BACK THE ASHES AFTER 14 YEARS.

1920–21   Aus 5 Eng 0
1921   Aus 3 Eng 0
1924–25   Aus 4 Eng 1
1926   Eng 1 Aus 0

Cumulative Ashes Head to Head
Tests - Aus 41 Eng 40
Series - Eng 16 Aus 10

ENG   AUS

THIS PERIOD SAW WARNER GUSHING ELOQUENTLY ABOUT THE GENTLEMAN'S GAME. "IT IS FUNDAMENTALLY NECESSARY THAT CRICKET SHOULD BE FREE FROM MALICE AND GUILE"

ALTHOUGH, WE HAVE ALL SEEN WHAT SORT OF PRACTICES EXISTED IN CRICKET EVEN IN THE SUPPOSED GOLDEN AGE. YET, THE MYTH OF THE GENTLEMAN'S GAME WAS CONSTRUCTED AT THAT TIME AND HAS BECOME INDESTRUCTIBLE BY NOW.

WARNER WAS NOT QUITE A STICKLER FOR FACTS. HE PUBLISHED MY IMAGINARY SCHOLARLY DISCOURSE ON THE USE OF SAWDUST IN WICKET PREPARATION IN *THE CRICKETER*

BERNARD HOLLOWOOD

THEN OF COURSE YOU HAD CARDUS. "IF EVERYTHING ELSE IN THIS NATION OF OURS WERE LOST BUT CRICKET — HER CONSTITUTION AND THE LAWS OF ENGLAND OF LORD HALSBURY — IT WOULD BE POSSIBLE TO RECONSTRUCT FROM THE THEORY AND PRACTICE OF CRICKET ALL THE ETERNAL ENGLISHNESS WHICH HAS GONE TO THE ESTABLISHMENT OF THAT CONSTITUTION AND LAWS AFORESAID." I KNOW PEOPLE STILL SWEAR BY HIM, AND OFTEN LOOK ASKANCE AT HIS CRITICS, BUT CAN ANYONE HONESTLY FIND ANY SENSE IN THOSE SPLENDIDLY WRITTEN WORDS?

ALL THE WHILE, ARMSTRONG WAS TAKING GAMESMANSHIP TO THE NEXT LEVEL, WHILE MAILEY AND DOUGLAS TELL US A LOT ABOUT BALL-TAMPERING OF THAT ERA.

SIGH...

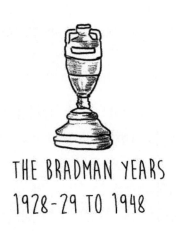

THE BRADMAN YEARS
1928-29 TO 1948

WE NOW ENTER AN ERA OF DOMINANCE BY ONE SOLITARY BATSMAN,
THE LIKE OF WHICH THE WORLD HAS NEVER SEEN BEFORE OR SINCE.

FOR TWO FULL DECADES THE WILLOW OF DON BRADMAN RULED CRICKET.
THESE MONUMENTAL RUN-SCORING DEEDS OF THIS ONE MAN RESULTED IN DESPERATE MEASURES
BY ENGLAND ... A DRAMATIC CHAPTER IN THE SAGA OF THE ASHES CALLED THE BODYLINE SERIES

THE RULES WERE NOT QUITE BROKEN, BUT THEY WERE STRETCHED TO LIMITS THAT RENDERED
THE GAME, THE ACTION AND THE FIELD, UNRECOGNIZABLE.

THERE WERE SEVERAL OTHER SUPREME GREATS OF THE GAME WHO PLAYED IN THIS ERA.
BUT, THESE 20 YEARS WERE ALL ABOUT THE BRADMAN PHENOMENON. BY THE END OF HIS
CAREER THE NUMBERS HE AMASSED BEGGARED BELIEF AND THE AUSTRALIAN SIDE BECAME
THE INVINCIBLES.

AND OF COURSE THERE WAS THE INTERLUDE WHEN THE GREATER GAME TOOK OVER FOR
ANOTHER SIX BLOODY YEARS. PLENTY OF CRICKETERS PARTICIPATED IN
THE SECOND WORLD WAR AND SEVERAL PERISHED INCLUDING THE GREAT HEDLEY VERITY.
CRICKET STARTED ALMOST IMMEDIATELY AFTER THE END OF THE WAR. THE GAME WAS
SEEN AS A CELEBRATION OF LIFE AT THE END OF THE MAYHEM, IN THE COURSE OF A
SPLENDID SERIES KNOWN AS THE VICTORY 'TESTS'.

1928-29 HAMMOND AND THE ENTRY OF BRADMAN

START OF A GREAT RIVALRY SPANNING TWO DECADES.
AFTER THE 1928-29 SERIES, WALLY HAMMOND
EMERGED AS THE BEST BATSMAN OF THE WORLD.
SADLY, HIS REIGN AT THE TOP WAS GOING TO BE SHORT.

LADIES ENCLOSURE

DRIVING THROUGH THE COVERS

WALLY HAMMOND SCORED A RECORD 905 RUNS WITH
2 DOUBLE HUNDREDS AND A PAIR OF CENTURIES IN EACH
INNINGS OF A TEST.

HE ALSO MANAGED TO TAKE TIME OFF
FOR HIS OTHER GREAT PASSION.
CELEBRATION OF BEAUTY
SOMETIMES WITH FIELD GLASSES

JACK, YOU SNARED MY RABBIT

SORRY, MAURICE

JACK WHITE

MAURICE TATE

BRADMAN'S DEBUT BROUGHT HIM JUST 18 AND 1.
HE WAS SUBJECTED TO SOME RIDICULE BY THE ENGLISH TEAM
AND DROPPED FROM THE SECOND TEST. AS BRADMAN CARRIED
THE DRINKS, HAMMOND HELPED HIMSELF TO A DOUBLE HUNDRED.

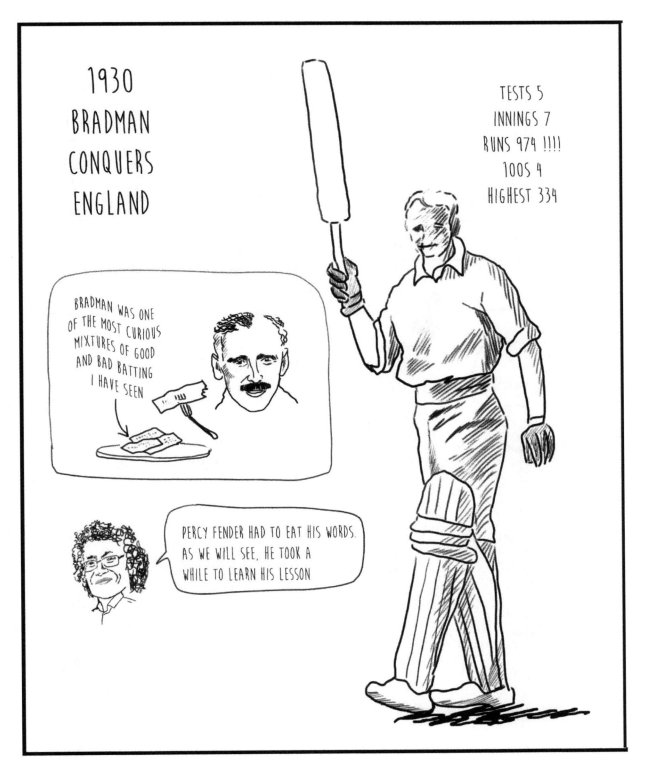

TRENT BRIDGE
BRADMAN FELL FOR 131 AND ENGLAND
TOOK THE LEAD...IT WOULD BE HIS SMALLEST
TEST HUNDRED BY FAR ON THIS TOUR

TRENT BRIDGE GROUNDSTAFF SYD COPLEY,
FIELDING AS SUBSTITUTE, TOOK AN
ASTONISHING CATCH TO DISMISS STAN MCCABE

THE BOY WAS
ALWAYS CARELESS

THE
OTHER
PERCY

KS DULEEPSINHJI SCORED 173 RUNS BEFORE HOLING OUT.
BUT BRADMAN'S REMARKABLE 254 SEALED THE ISSUE.

AUSTRALIA DREW LEVEL AT
LORD'S IN ONE OF THE BEST
TEST MATCHES OF ALL TIME

THIS GAME COULD BE LAID
UP IN HEAVEN, A PLATONIC
IDEA OF CRICKET
IN PERFECTION

LEEDS
BRADMAN SCORED 105
BEFORE LUNCH AND
309 ON THE FIRST DAY

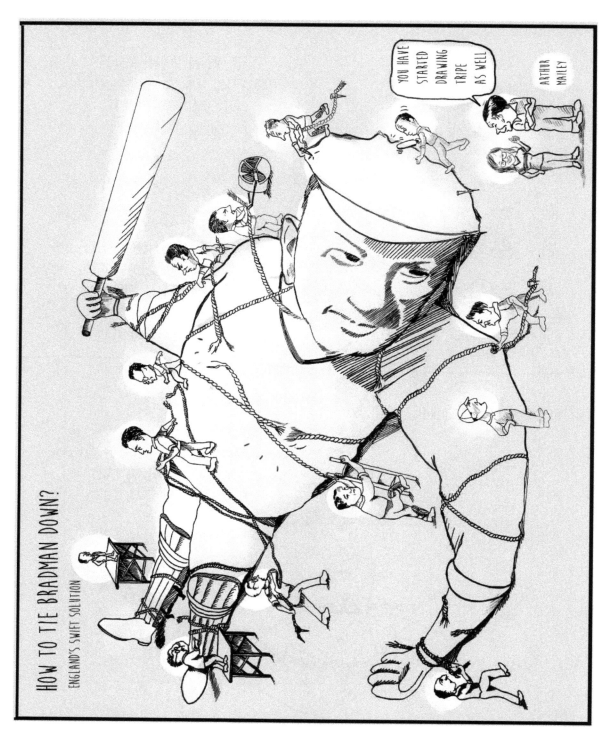

BODYLINE

The Ashes

119

IT WAS THE FIRST SERIES IN WHICH RADIO PLAYED A BIG ROLE IN BROADCASTING CRICKET.

ALAN FAIRFAX

BRADMAN WAS ONE OF THE SEVERAL BIG NAMES CONTRACTED TO PROVIDE BULLETINS. ALAN FAIRFAX EVEN COBBLED TOGETHER A DELAYED COMMENTARY FROM CABLED INFORMATION, FOR RADIO PARIS, PERCHED IN A BOOTH IN THE EIFFEL TOWER.

MCCABE

BRADMAN

KIPPAX

NOBLE

ERNIE JONES

RICHARDSON

AN' I RECKON (SAID DAD) THAT A MAN'S WORST PESTS IS THIS HERE WIRELESS AN' THESE HERE TESTS

THE AUSTRALIANS FIRST BEHELD THE FULL FLEDGED ENGLISH TECHNIQUES IN THE FIFTH TOUR MATCH, A STRONG AUSTRALIAN XI VS MCC AT MELBOURNE. JARDINE WAS NOWHERE TO BE SEEN. BOB WYATT WAS IN CHARGE WHILE JARDINE WAS HAVING A TROUT FISHING BREAK WITH THREE FRIENDS 200 MILES AWAY IN THE BOGONG VALLEY

DAVID FRITH

HE DELIBERATLEY ABSENTED HIMSELF, IN CASE THE PLAN BACKFIRED

BILL O'REILLY KEPT SAYING FOR SEVERAL YEARS

MY BAIT HAS BEEN SET

LEFT HANDED O'BRIEN OPENED WITH BILL WOODFULL AND WAS CONFUSED BY THE FIELD

BUT IT IS THE RIGHT-HANDER DOWN THAT END. I AM THE LEFT-HANDER

THE REPORTS OF THE ENGLAND BOWLING WERE SCATHING

TRUTH

STORK HENDRY: MELBOURNE:

Larwood was trying to decapitate Bradman and Woodfull, while Jardine, captain of all the bally old cricketahs, went trout fishing

The Ashes

GUBBY ALLEN WROTE TO HIS PARENTS:

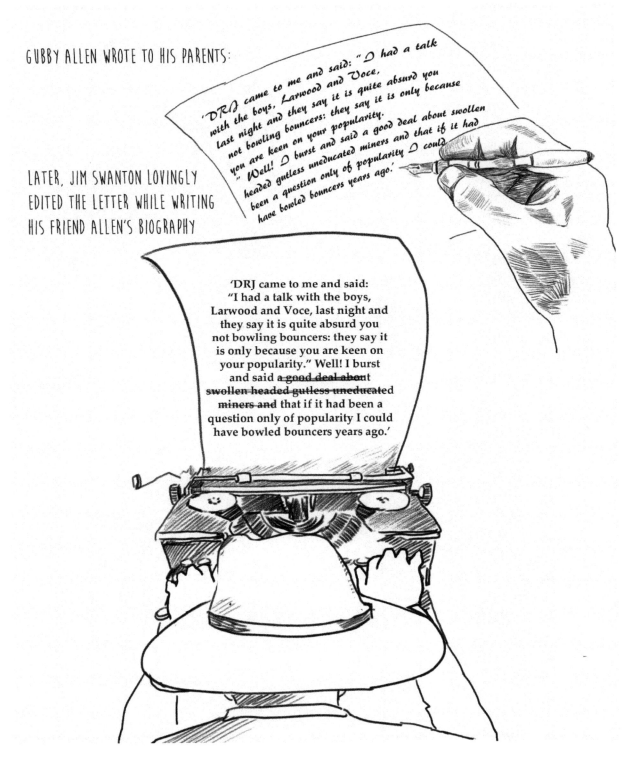

LATER, JIM SWANTON LOVINGLY
EDITED THE LETTER WHILE WRITING
HIS FRIEND ALLEN'S BIOGRAPHY

'DRJ came to me and said:
"I had a talk with the boys,
Larwood and Voce, last night and
they say it is quite absurd you
not bowling bouncers: they say it
is only because you are keen on
your popularity." Well! I burst
and said a good deal about
swollen headed gutless uneducated
miners and that if it had been a
question only of popularity I could
have bowled bouncers years ago.'

ALLEN WAS AN ETON-CAMBRIDGE-EDUCATED,
CLASS-CONSCIOUS SNOB.
HE WAS A HYPOCRITE TO BOOT.
HE WROTE SPITEFUL LETTERS ABOUT
JARDINE, ALL THE WHILE SMILING
AWAY BESIDE HIM IN TOUR PHOTOGRAPHS.

SWANTON TRIES TO PAPER OVER THIS CRACK BY
ALLUDING TO A LETTER IN WHICH ALLEN WRITES:
"I COULD HAVE BOWLED BODYLINE THOUGH NOT SO
WELL AS HAROLD." THERE IS NO SUCH LETTER IN
EXISTENCE. THE VOICE OF
ESTABLISHMENT WAS JUST DOING
THE FACE OF ESTABLISHMENT
A FAVOUR THERE BY
INVENTING SOME FACTS.

AS I SAID AT
THE TIME, JIM?

ALMOST, GUBBY.
WHAT ANY SORT OF A
CRICKET PERSON WOULD
LIKE TO READ

FELLOW AMATEUR BOB WYATT
HAD A DIFFERENT TAKE ON ALLEN'S
REFUSAL TO BOWL BODYLINE

ALLEN ACTUALLY
LACKED THE ACCURACY
TO BOWL LEG-THEORY.

SUTCLIFFE (194), HAMMOND (112), AND PATAUDI (VERY CAUTIOUS 102) HELPED ENGLAND TO 524

AUSTRALIA WERE BLOWN AWAY BY A SUPERFAST LARWOOD IN THE SECOND INNINGS, BOWLING WITH A LOADED LEG-SIDE FIELD.

EVEN AFTER THE 10-WICKET DEFEAT, AUSTRALIAN CAPTAIN BILL WOODFULL REFUSED TO CONSIDER RETALIATING IN A SIMILAR WAY. HOWEVER, CRITICISM FOR THE ENGLISH TACTICS WAS EVERYWHERE. IN THE PRESS, PUBLIC AND ALSO IN SHOW BUSINESS.

THEY MADE SOME EASY MONEY WITH THIS DRIVEL

NOW THIS KIND OF CRICKET...
BRUISES AND FRACTURES GALORE
AFTER INSURING THEIR LIVES
BATSMEN WALK OUT TO SCORE...
UNDERTAKERS LOOK ON
WITH BROAD GRINS
OH, THEY'D BE A LOT CALMER,
IN NED KELLY'S ARMOUR,
WHEN LARWOOD THE WRECKER BEGINS

WHY IS IT CALLED LARWOOD COCKTAIL?

BECAUSE IT ALWAYS GOES TO YOUR HEAD...

OOOH...

WELL, I'LL BE FOOCKED

THE DON PULLED THE FIRST BALL HE FACED AND INSIDE EDGED IT ON TO HIS STUMPS. IT REMAINED THE MOST FAMOUS DUCK TILL 1948. FOR ONCE, EVEN JARDINE, 'THE SPHYNX' SHOWED SOME EMOTION.

WITH THE DON GONE, AUSTRALIA FINISHED WITH AN UNIMPRESSIVE 228

DON WILL SET THIS RIGHT, EH? SO... WHEN IS THIS DON OF YOURS COMING IN?

CRITICISM OF THE ENGLISH TACTICS AFFECTED MANAGER PLUM WARNER. BUT, THERE WERE OTHER EVENTS TO LIFT HIS SPIRITS.

ENJOYING YOURSELF, MR WARNER?

EH?

OH, YOU KNOW MY NAME ALREADY!

I HOPE YOUR EYESIGHT AND HEARING ARE FINE GEORGE. YOU'LL NEED BOTH. I'M AFTER THEM TODAY.

SPIRIT OF THE GAME, BILL. ANOTHER 7 DECADES AND I WOULD HAVE YOU REPORTED TO THE ICC FOR GROSS MISCONDUCT.

BUT WITH BILL O'REILLY PICKING UP 5 WICKETS, THE ENGLISH COULD RESPOND WITH JUST 169.

The Ashes

30 Jan
TELEGRAM 8 FEB
WE DONOT REGARD THE UNSPORTSMANSHIP OF
YOUR TEAM AS BEING IN QUESTION
THIS PARTICULAR CLASS OF BOWLING NOT
IN THE BEST INTEREST OF CRICKET
WE HOPE THE REMAINING TESTS WILL BE
PLAYED WITH THE TRADITIONAL GOOD FEELING
LARWOOD'S BOWLING
MAY AFFECT FATE OF NATIONS,
LEG TRAPS MAY IMPERIL
IMPERIAL RELATIONS
DIMLY ONE CAN SEE THE PROCESS
SAY IF THE BRITISH EXPORTS FALL
IF YOU'LL GIVE US FURTHER PREFERENCE,
LARWOOD SHALL NOT BOWL AT ALL
IF THE TEST MATCH SHOULD BE CANCELLED,
WE SHALL TAX AT HIGHER RATE
ALL AUSTRALIA HAS TO SEND US,
TO RECOUP THE VANISHED 'GATE'
-MACFLECKNOE
BY THE BEARD OF GRACE, THEY STILL BELIEVE THE GAME HAS A SPIRIT.
AND THEY WILL CONTINUE TO BELIEVE IT. IN FACT THEY'D GO ON TO NAME A LECTURE AFTER IT

A YEAR EARLIER, ABORIGINAL FAST BOWLER EDDIE GILBERT HAD FLOORED DON BRADMAN BEFORE DISMISSING HIM FOR A DUCK, A SPELL THE MASTER SAID WAS THE FASTEST HE EVER FACED

THERE WAS SPECULATION THAT HE WOULD BE SELECTED FOR AUSTRALIA TO COUNTER BODYLINE

IN THE TOUR MATCH BETWEEN QUEENSLAND AND MCC IMMEDIATELY BEFORE THE FOURTH TEST, HE BOWLED A DECENT SPELL, STRIKING JARDINE PAINFULLY ON THE HIP-BONE MUCH TO THE DELIGHT OF THE CROWD. THE ENGLAND CAPTAIN COLLAPSED ON REACHING THE DRESSING ROOM.

HOWEVER, ULTIMATELY HE WAS NOT SELECTED

IN HIS TIME, SOME TEAMMATES REFUSED TO SPEAK TO GILBERT, SHARE TAXIS, DINING TABLES, ROOMS. HE WAS HANDED A FRACTION OF HIS MONEY WHILE THE REST WAS DEPOSITED TO HIS ACCOUNT, SINCE HE WAS A 'COMIC SAVAGE PRONE TO ABANDONING THE SIDE.'
HE WASN'T ALLOWED TO SLEEP WITH THE TEAM AND WAS PUT UP IN A TENT ON THE PRACTICE PITCH

GILBERT DIED AT THE WOLSTON PARK HOSPITAL NEAR BRISBANE AGED 72 AFTER MANY YEARS OF ILL HEALTH DUE TO ALCOHOLISM AND MENTAL ILLNESS

VOCE MISSED THE BRISBANE TEST BECAUSE OF INFLUENZA. WITHOUT HIS PARTNER, THE TROUBLESOME HEAT AND HUMIDITY, LARWOOD SEEMED LESS EFFECTIVE WITH HIS BODYLINE FIELD. AUSTRALIA REACHED 251/3 BY THE END OF THE FIRST DAY, LEADING TO PREMATURE CELEBRATION IN THE PRESS.

GOING BACK TO THE MINES WILL BE A VACATION AFTER THIS SERIES.

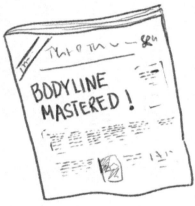

BODYLINE MASTERED !

IF A SCHOOLBOY TRIED TO CUT A BALL ON THE LEG STICK YOU WOULD SMACK HIS HEAD, YET HERE WAS BRADMAN DOING IT

BUT ON THE SECOND MORNING, PEPPED BY UNUSUAL STIMULANTS, LARWOOD DISMISSED BRADMAN FOR 76. AUSTRALIA MANAGED 340, AS THE FAST BOWLER FINISHED WITH 4 WICKETS.

HOBBS HOWEVER DID NOT COME OUT AS HARSHLY IN HIS NEWSPAPER REPORTS ABOUT THE TACTICS EMPLOYED BY JARDINE

EXCELLENT HAROLD, YOU DESERVE THREE CHEERS FOR THAT.

THE HERO OF THE MATCH EXPERIENCED THE MODERN MARVEL OF A TRANS-CONTINENTAL PHONE CALL FROM WIFE MAY IN MANCHESTER.

EDDIE, ARE YOU OUT OF YOUR MIND? STAY OUT OF THE SUN.

SHE'S SWEET. BUT, IF GRAHAM BELL HAD A WIFE LIKE THAT HE'D NEVER HAVE INVENTED THIS BALLY CONTRAPTION.

AS LARWOOD CONTINUED TO TERRORISE THE AUSTRALIAN BATSMEN, IT WAS PAYNTER WHO FINISHED THINGS OFF WITH A SIX IN THE SECOND INNINGS TO ENSURE AN 8-WICKET WIN.

THE DESPERATELY SAD NEWS OF THE DEATH OF THE BRILLIANT ARCHIE JACKSON, JUST 23, CAST A SHADOW OVER THE LAST DAY.

ARCHIE JACKSON
BORN 5 SEP 1909
DIED 16 FEB 1933

JACKSON IS STILL THE YOUNGEST TO SCORE AN ASHES HUNDRED, AT 19 YEARS 152 DAYS. HE REMAINS THE YOUNGEST ASHES CRICKETER TO DIE

FIFTH TEST

LARWOOD ASKED JARDINE TO BE EXCUSED FROM THE FINAL TEST AT SYDNEY. HOWEVER, THE CAPTAIN DISAGREED

I'VE BOWLED MY INSIDE OUT AND WE'VE WON THE ASHES. COULD I SIT THIS TEST OUT, MR JARDINE?

NO, HAROLD. WE'VE GOT THE BASTARDS DOWN THERE, AND WE'LL KEEP THEM THERE.

INJURED OR NOT, LARWOOD PICKED UP THE FIRST THREE WICKETS, INCLUDING BRADMAN FOR 48 AS THE DON ONCE AGAIN MOVED AROUND IN THE CREASE, THIS TIME TOWARDS THE OFF-SIDE TO GLANCE TOWARDS THE LEG.

HE CAN BOWL ME, BUT HE CAN'T HIT ME.

ENGLAND EXPECTS MY FOOT!!

IN ALL LARWOOD PICKED UP 4 FOR 98 IN 32 OVERS AS AUSTRALIA TOTALLED 435. BUT, THERE WAS A SURPRISE WAITING FOR HIM AT THE END OF THE SECOND DAY.

REALLY? ME? NOW A NIGHT-WATCHMAN, MR JARDINE?

YOU ARE HANDY WITH THE BAT, HAROLD.

HANDY? WHAT ABOUT MY FOOT?

BULLSEYE!

FINALLY, IN THE SECOND INNINGS, LARWOOD HIT BRADMAN FOR THE FIRST TIME IN THE SERIES. A MOMENT BRADMAN HAD VOWED WOULD NEVER COME.

BRADMAN MOVED AROUND, EXPOSING HIS STUMPS IN A RISKY MANNER, BUT LARWOOD WAS TOO ANXIOUS TO CLAIM A HIT ON HIM TO AIM FOR THE STUMPS.

FANCY THE SKIPPER PATTING LARWOOD BACK. I'D HAVE HELPED MYSELF TO 20 RUNS.

BILL O'REILLY

BUT LARWOOD ENDED HAVING TO COMPLETE HIS LAST OVER BOWLING FROM A STATIONARY POSITION, SO PAINFUL WAS HIS FOOT INJURY.

BUT JARDINE WOULD NOT ALLOW HIM TO LEAVE THE GROUND.

I CAN'T RUN, I'M USELESS. I'LL HAVE TO GO OFF.

HE WAS ALLOWED TO LEAVE THE FIELD ONLY AFTER BRADMAN HAD BEEN BOWLED BY VERITY FOR 71

FIELD AT COVER POINT. THERE'S A MAN COVERING YOU THERE. YOU CAN'T GO OFF WHILE THIS LITTLE BASTARD'S IN.

LARWOOD NEVER PLAYED FOR ENGLAND AGAIN.
HIS PRESENCE IN THE TEAM WOULD HAVE
CAUSED A LOT OF CONTROVERSY.

BESIDES, HIS GHOSTED ACCOUNT OF THE
1932-33 SERIES, 'BODYLINE?', WAS BRUTAL
IN ITS ASSESSMENT OF AUSTRALIAN BATSMEN,
AND MUCH OF IT WAS WRITTEN WITHOUT THE
FAST BOWLER'S REVIEW.

THE BODYLINE SERIES WAS LAST
THAT THE TEST CRICKET WORLD
SAW OF THIS GREAT BOWLER

DOUGLAS JARDINE LED ENGLAND AGAINST
WEST INDIES AT HOME AND THEN IN INDIA.
BUT PRESSURE MOUNTED ON HIM AS MCC GREW
UNEASY ABOUT THE REACTION OF THE
AUSTRALIANS IF HE CONTINUED TO BE
THE ENGLAND CAPTAIN. THE SITUATION
WAS RESOLVED WHEN JARDINE MADE
HIMSELF UNAVAILABLE FOR SELECTION
STATING BUSINESS COMMITMENTS.

PLUM WARNER ON RETURN HEAPED PRAISES ON THE ENGLAND CAPTAIN, AND ALSO LARWOOD FOR HIS MAGNIFICENT FAST BOWLING BUT IN THE BACKGROUND HE WAS AN INFLUENTIAL HAND THAT WROTE THE CRICKETING DEATH SENTENCE OF LARWOOD AND JARDINE. IN 1937, AFTER THE DUST OF BODYLINE HAD SETTLED, WARNER RECEIVED KNIGHTHOOD FOR HIS SERVICES TO CRICKET.

JARDINE WAS THE BEST CAPTAIN ENGLAND COULD HAVE, LARWOOD THE BEST FAST BOWLER. BUT THEY WERE NOT AVAILABLE AFTER ALL THAT CONTROVERSY OVER FAST LEG-THEORY.

CYRIL WALTERS

WYATT WAS OUT WITH A BROKEN THUMB, AND GUBBY ALLEN WAS RECOVERING FROM AN APPENDICITIS OPERATION. 6-TEST-OLD CF WALTERS WAS MADE CAPTAIN, DESPITE THERE BEING PLAYERS OF THE STATURE OF HAMMOND AND SUTCLIFFE IN THE SIDE. BIZARRE, BUT THAT'S WHAT AMATEUR-PROFESSIONAL DIVIDE OFTEN RESULTED IN.

HAMMOND AND SUTCLIFFE WERE TWO OF THE MOST SUCCESSFUL BATSMEN OF ENGLAND EVER. NEITHER WAS KNIGHTED. FAR LESSER ENGLISH CRICKETERS WERE. HAMMOND HAD TO TURN AN AMATEUR IN ORDER TO CAPTAIN THE SIDE. SUTCLIFFE NEVER LED ENGLAND.

NEVILLE CARDUS TOOK EXCEPTION TO SUTCLIFFE'S SPEAKING NOT WITH THE ACCENTS OF YORKSHIRE BUT OF TEDDINGTON

ERIC MIDWINTER

CARDUS SAW THE ADVENT OF THE LIKES OF SUTCLIFFE AND HAMMOND WITH THEIR SAVILLE ROW SUITS AS THE SIGNS OF THE IMMINENT COLLAPSE OF THE OLD FEUDAL SYSTEM

THE COUNTY CRICKETER HAS IN CERTAIN INSTANCES BECOME A MAN OF BOURGEOIS PROFESSION

1934

WARNED YOU. THE ATMOSPHERE IS ELECTRIC.

THE TRENT BRIDGE TEST WAS WON BY AUSTRALIA WITH JUST 10 MINUTES TO SPARE. GRIMMETT AND O'REILLY CLAIMED 19 OF THE 20 ENGLISH WICKETS.

BILL O'REILLY BOWLED AUSTRALIA TO A 238-RUN WIN WITH AN 11-WICKET HAUL AS WALTERS LED ENGLAND.

HE WAS THE DADDY OF THEM ALL. I PUT HIM ABOVE BARNES BECAUSE HE HAD A GOOGLY."

GOOGLY? I NEVER NEEDED ONE

The Ashes

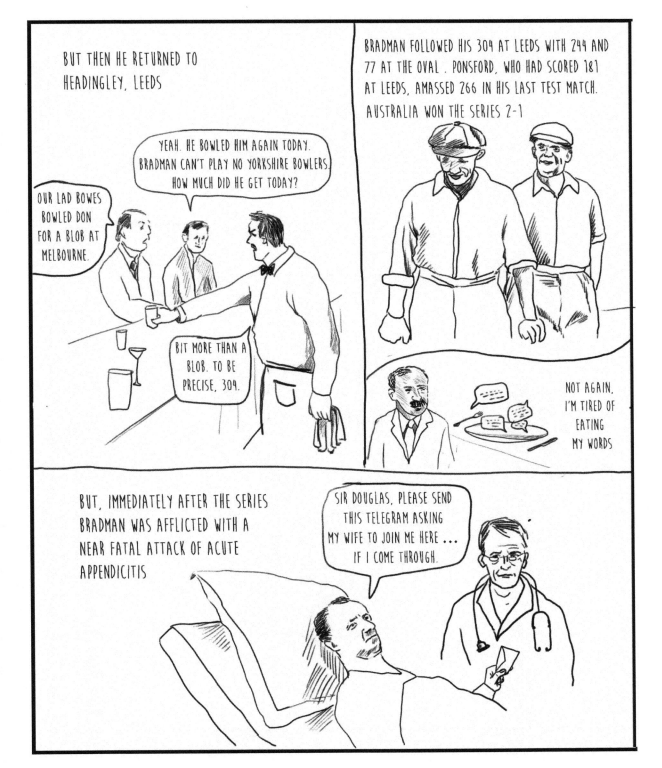

THE DON SCORED ANOTHER DUCK IN THE SECOND TEST AT SYDNEY. THE AUSTRALIANS TOTALLED 80 ON ANOTHER STICKY WICKET. ALTHOUGH HE SCORED 82 IN THE SECOND INNINGS, BRADMAN WAS OUT TO A WILD HOOK WITH HIS HEAD IN THE AIR. HAMMOND'S 231 WON THE MATCH FOR ENGLAND.

THE WICKET WAS NOT PARTICULARLY BAD TO BAT ON. MOST OF THE AUSTRALIANS GOT THEMSELVES OUT DURING THE STORM IN THE NIGHT.

BRADMAN'S STROKEPLAY WAS NOT FIT FOR PUBLIC VIEW.

THE GREATEST RUN-GETTER IN THE HISTORY OF CRICKET HAS MADE THE WORST STROKE IN THE HISTORY OF CRICKET.

TWO DUCKS? SOMEONE IS BOUND TO SUFFER AS A RESULT.

VIC RICHARDSON

CARDUS

C B FRY

MAURICE LEYLAND

WITH AUSTRALIA STILL 0-2 DOWN, AND BRADMAN ALREADY CRITICISED FOR CHOOSING WARD OVER GRIMMETT, THE CRIES WERE LOUD FOR THE DON TO BE RELIEVED OF CAPTAINCY. IT DID NOT HELP THAT THE BOARD SUMMONED MCCABE, O'REILLY, FLEETWOOD-SMITH AND O'BRIEN FOR A DISCIPLINARY HEARING AND WARNED AGAINST TOO MUCH ALCOHOL.

DON, WHY HAVE WE BEEN SUMMONED?

THE B**** PROTESTANT WAS ALWAYS AGAINST US IRISH CATHOLICS

I BET THIS LITTLE TEE-TOTALLER IS BEHIND ALL THIS.

NO IDEA. I HAVEN'T BEEN INVITED TO THE MEETING.

The Ashes

AUSTRALIA GAINED A HANDY FIRST INNINGS LEAD AT MELBOURNE IN SPITE OF BRADMAN SCORING 13. AFTER BOWLING ENGLAND OUT FOR 76 ON A STICKY, BRADMAN REVERSED THE BATTING ORDER. COMING IN AT NO 7, HE BATTED FOR 7 HOURS AND 38 MINUTES TO SCORE 270. IT WAS CHOSEN BY WISDEN AS THE BEST INNINGS OF THE CENTURY.

THE BRADMAN FIRE BLAZED FORTH, THREATENING TO CONSUME ENGLAND.

BRADMAN FOLLOWED IT UP WITH 212 AT ADELAIDE AND 169 AT MELBOURNE.

I TOLD YOU SO.

IF I WAS A SELECTOR I WOULD COUNT HIM AS TWO BATSMEN.

BRADMAN IS THE 8TH WONDER OF THE WORLD.

LEYLAND

HAMMOND

C B FRY

FATHER FORGIVE THEM, FOR THEY KNOW NOT WHICH 7 THEY CHOOSE

THAT WAS NOT A WIDE!

164

1938   903 FOR 7 AND ALL THAT

DON BRADMAN'S AUSTRALIANS VISITED ENGLAND.
WAITING FOR THEM WAS WALLY HAMMOND AND HIS YOUNG BRIGADE.

HAMMOND HAD TURNED AMATEUR AND THUS BECOME CAPTAIN OF ENGLAND. IN HIS TEAM THERE WERE SOME SUPREMELY TALENTED YOUNGSTERS INCLUDING LEN HUTTON DENIS COMPTON AND BILL EDRICH.

HOWEVER, THERE WERE OTHER OMINOUS FIGURES AROUND THE WORLD AS WELL

WAR IS NOT A GAME OF CRICKET

GEORGE ORWELL

COME AND LOOK AT THIS. YOU MAY NEVER SEE ANYTHING LIKE THIS AGAIN.

AT TRENT BRIDGE CENTURIES WERE STRUCK BY THE YOUNG DUO OF LEN HUTTON AND DENIS COMPTON.
EDDIE PAYNTER AND CHARLIE BARNETT ALSO HELPED THEMSELVES TO HUNDREDS.
STAN MCCABE SAVED AUSTRALIA WITH A MAGNIFICENT 232

IN FAREWELL TO CRICKET, DON BRADMAN WROTE: "LEONARD HUTTON AND DENIS COMPTON EACH MADE A CENTURY, EACH WAS PLAYING IN HIS FIRST TEST MATCH"

BOTH HUTTTON AND COMPTON HAD MADE THEIR DEBUTS AGAINST NEW ZEALAND IN 1937. HOWEVER, ASHES AND TEST MATCHES WERE STILL QUITE SYNONYMOUS

AT LORD'S CRICKET WAS TELECAST LIVE FOR THE FIRST TIME IN HISTORY. WALLY HAMMOND CELEBRATED THE OCCASION WITH A DOUBLE HUNDRED, A KNOCK FIT FOR KINGS.

HE'S HITTING SO HARD. ARE YOU SURE THE BALL WON'T DAMAGE THE TELEVISION SCREEN?

BILL BROWN HIT 205 IN THE FIRST INNINGS AND BRADMAN 102 NOT OUT IN THE SECOND AS THE MATCH ENDED IN A DRAW. BROWN AND BRADMAN ARE THE ONLY AUSSIES TO SCORE MULTIPLE HUNDREDS AT LORD'S

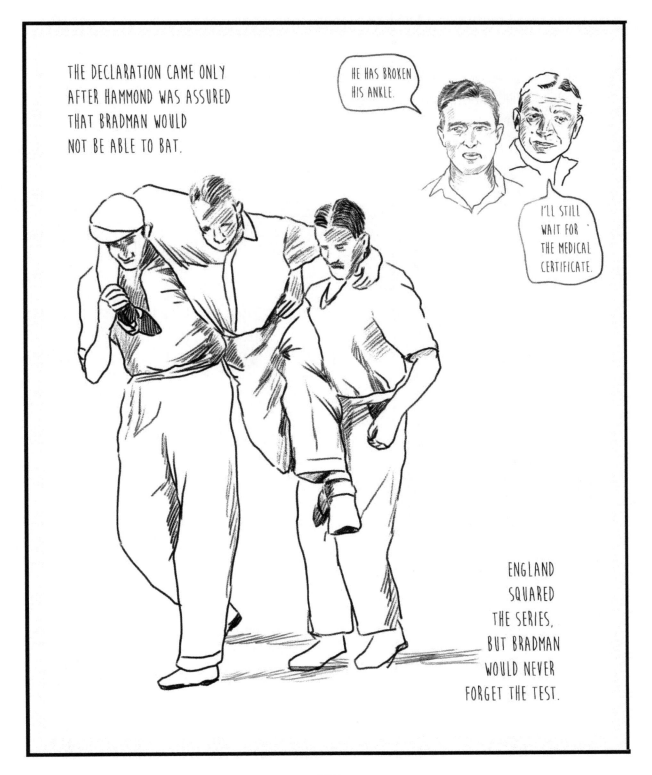

MILLER
HUTTON
COMPTON
BOWES
ONCE AGAIN HUNDREDS AND HUNDREDS OF CRICKETERS VOLUNTEERED.
CRICKETING METAPHORS WERE USED THROUGHOUT THE WAR.
HIT ROMMEL FOR SIX OUT OF AFRICA
GENERAL MONTGOMERY
LORD'S BOMBED?? AUSTRALIANS WILL ALWAYS FIGHT FOR THOSE 22 YARDS. LORD'S AND IT'S TRADITIONS BELONG TO AUSTRALIA JUST AS MUCH AS ENGLAND
AUSTRALIAN PRIME MINISTER JOHN CURTIN
PONSFORD IS OUT, BUT BRADMAN IS STILL BATTING.
MUSSOLINI DEAD

IMMEDIATELY AFTER THE WAR, 5 VICTORY 'TESTS' WERE PLAYED BETWEEN ENGLAND AND AUSTRALIAN SERVICES.

CONTESTED BY GREAT NAMES, PLAYED IN THE BEST OF SPIRITS AND WITH MOST ATTRACTIVE CRICKET ON DISPLAY, THESE GAMES COMMUNICATED TO THE WAR RAVAGED AND TRAUMATISED ENGLISH CITIZENS THAT THINGS WERE BACK TO NORMAL AGAIN.

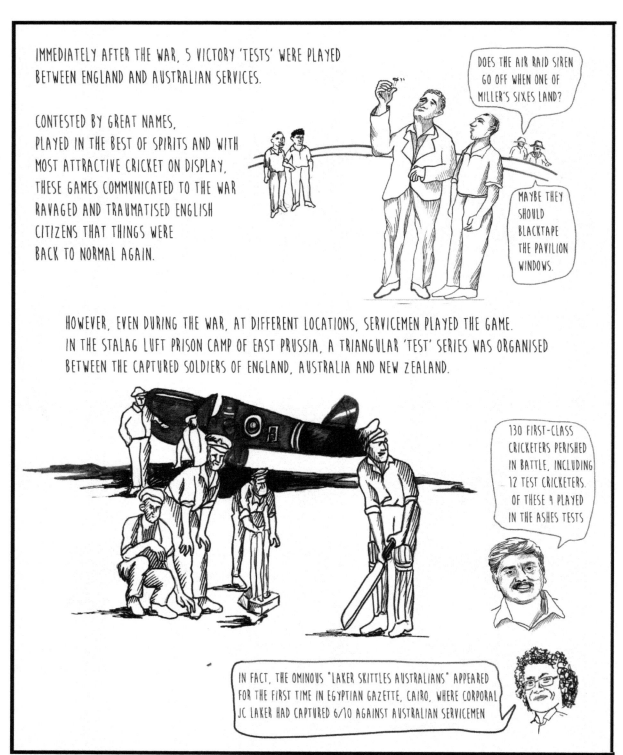

HOWEVER, EVEN DURING THE WAR, AT DIFFERENT LOCATIONS, SERVICEMEN PLAYED THE GAME. IN THE STALAG LUFT PRISON CAMP OF EAST PRUSSIA, A TRIANGULAR 'TEST' SERIES WAS ORGANISED BETWEEN THE CAPTURED SOLDIERS OF ENGLAND, AUSTRALIA AND NEW ZEALAND.

HEDLEY VERITY

ONE OF THE GREATEST LEFT-ARM SPINNERS EVER, VERITY DISMISSED DON BRADMAN 8 TIMES, MORE THAN ANY OTHER BOWLER. IN 40 TESTS HE CAPTURED 144 WICKETS AT 24.37 APIECE. HIS 59 ASHES WICKETS CAME AT 28.06 EACH.

COMMANDING THE GREEN HOWARDS IN A NIGHT ATTACK ON THE PLAINS OF CATANIA, VERITY WAS HIT ON THE CHEST. HIS LAST ORDER WAS 'KEEP GOING'.

CAPTURED BY THE GERMANS, HE DIED AT CASERTA, ITALY. HIS GRAVE IN THE CASERTA WAR CEMETERY WAS VISITED BY HUTTON'S ENGLISHMEN IN 1954.

IN A TRAGIC COINCIDENCE, VERITY, THE GREATEST LEFT-ARM SPINNER OF HIS ERA, FOLLOWED THE FOOTSTEPS OF COLIN BLYTHE, THE GREATEST LEFT-ARM SPINNER OF HIS ERA, WHO DIED IN THE FIRST WORLD WAR.

MACAULAY WAS A YORKSHIRE PACE BOWLER WHO PLAYED 468 FIRST-CLASS MATCHES, INCLUDING 8 TESTS FOR ENGLAND. A HANDY BATSMAN AS WELL, HIS SOLITARY ASHES APPEARANCE WAS AT LEEDS IN 1926 WHEN HE WENT FOR A LOT OF RUNS BUT SCORED 76 WITH THE BAT FROM NO 10, ADDING 108 WITH GEORGE GEARY. IN 15 TESTS HE CAPTURED 24 WICKETS AT 27.58 AND SCORED 112 RUNS AT 18.66. HE DIED OF PNEUMONIA DUE TO THE WET COLD WEATHER IN SHETLAND ISLANDS WHERE HE HAD BEEN POSTED.

GEORGE
MACAULAY

A SCHOOL TEACHER, FAST BOWLER, WONDERFUL WRITER AND PASSIONATE PAINTER AND ARTIST, FARNES WAS ONE OF THE MOST INTERESTING SOULS NIPPED IN THE BUD. HIS CAREER ENDED AT 28, AND LIFE AT 30. HIS 15 TESTS GOT HIM 60 WICKETS AT 28.65, AN AVERAGE ALMOST IDENTICAL TO THE AUSTRALIAN FAST BOWLER TIBBY COTTER WHO PERISHED IN THE FRST WORLD WAR. HIS 38 ASHES WICKETS CAME AT 28.02. COMMISSIONED FROM SERGEANT TO PILOT OFFICER IN SEPTEMBER 1941, HE WAS KILLED IN AN ACCIDENT DURING A NIGHT FLIGHT NEAR CHIPPING WARDEN IN OXFORDSHIRE.

KEN
FARNES

GREGORY PLAYED JUST TWO TESTS. BOTH WERE DURING THE RIVETING 1936-37 ASHES SERIES. ON DEBUT HE WAS ASSOCIATED IN A 135-RUN PARTNERSHIP WITH DON BRADMAN. HIS SCORES WERE 23, 50 AND 80; GIVING HIM 153 RUNS IN ALL AT 51.00 HE DIED AT 26, HIS BOSTON BOMBER CAUGHT IN A STORM OVER EAST BENGAL WHILE ON A MISSION TO BOMB BURMA.

ROSS GREGORY

POST-WAR

MILLER'S PROCLAMATIONS ABOUT CRICKET AND WAR DID NOT PREVENT HIM FROM BOWLING FIERCE BOUNCERS AT LEN HUTTON, THE BEST BATSMAN OF ENGLAND WHO HAD AN ARM SHORTENED DUE TO AN INJURY SUSTAINED DURING WAR TIME TRAINING.

IT'S ANOTHER BLITZ ATTACK.

IT NEEDED JUST MILD COAXING OF BRADMAN TO EGG HIM ON.

A COUPLE OF BUMPERS WON'T MAKE THE SELECTORS DROP YOU.

THEY ARE USING TOMMY-GUNS, WE WATER-PISTOLS.

HAMMOND, THE CAPTAIN, AT 43, A PALE SHADOW OF HIS GREAT SELF, GENERALLY DROVE AROUND IN HIS JAGUAR, AWAY FROM THE TEAM.

not Marsham tyres

MILLER
RUNS 384
AVE 76.8
WKTS 16
AVE 20.9

BARNES
RUNS 443
AVE 73.8

LINDWALL
WKTS 18
AVE 20.4

BRADMAN
RUNS 680
AVE 97.1

MORRIS
RUNS 503
AVE 71.8

COMPTON
RUNS 459
AVE 51.0

EDRICH
RUNS 462
AVE 46.2

HUTTON
RUNS 417
AVE 46.3

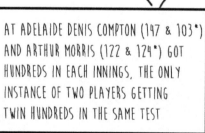

AT ADELAIDE DENIS COMPTON (147 & 103*)
AND ARTHUR MORRIS (122 & 124*) GOT
HUNDREDS IN EACH INNINGS, THE ONLY
INSTANCE OF TWO PLAYERS GETTING
TWIN HUNDREDS IN THE SAME TEST

FOR A LOT OF OTHER ENGLISHMEN, THE
TOUR WAS SUCCESSFUL IN OTHER WAYS.
SOME EVEN SENT FOOD PACKETS BACK
TO THEIR FAMILIES IN ENGLAND

BURP !

AUS 3
ENG 0

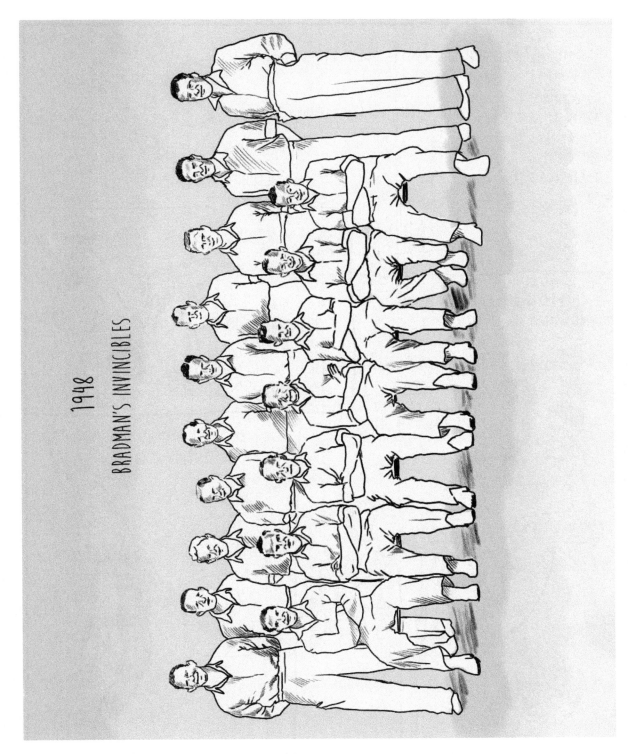

The Ashes

TOO MANY BUMPERS, DON

YOU HAVE A BAT, DON'T YOU?

THAT'S NOT WHAT YOU SAID DURING BODYLINE

TRENTBRIDGE AUS 1 ENG 0
BRADMAN GOT HIS USUAL 100
COMPTON HAD COMPLAINTS

MILLER REFUSED TO BOWL, TOSSING THE BALL BACK TO HIS SKIPPER.

LORD'S
AUS 2 ENG 0

FIND SOMEONE ELSE TO BOWL, DON. MY BACK HURTS

BARNES WAS STRUCK BY POLLARD WHILE HE FIELDED TOO CLOSE TO THE WICKET

COMPTON (2 HUNDREDS IN THE SERIES) WAS STRUCK ON THE HEAD BY LINDWALL

OLD TRAFFORD
ACCIDENTAL DRAW

BRADMAN AND MORRIS CHASED DOWN AN UNPRECEDENTED 404. AUSTRALIA WON BY 7 WICKETS.

MORRIS 182
BRADMAN 173*

BRADMAN AT LEEDS
TESTS 4
RUNS 963
AVE 192.6

HEADINGLEY AUS 3 ENG 0

ENG 52 ALL OUT
HUTTON C TALLON B LINDWALL 30

THE OVAL
AUS 4 ENG 0

WHEN BRADMAN CAME IN TO BAT AT THE OVAL, ENGLAND SKIPPER NORMAN YARDLEY GATHERED HIS MEN AROUND TO GIVE HIM THREE CHEERS.

CAREER
T 52
R 6996
AVE 99.94
100S 29

ASHES
T 37
R 5028
AVE 89.78
100S 19

AS CAPTAIN
WON 15
LOST 3
DRAW 6

AS ASHES
CAPTAIN
WON 11
LOST 3
DRAW 5

1928–29 Eng 4 Aus 1
1930   Aus 2 Eng 1
1932–33 Eng 4 Aus 1
1934   Aus 2 Eng 1
1936–37 Aus 3 Eng 2
1938   Eng 1 Aus 1
1946–47 Aus 3 Eng 0
1948   Aus 4 Eng 0

Cumulative Ashes Head to Head
Tests - Aus 58 Eng 53
Series - Eng 18 Aus 15

ENG   AUS

END OF AN ERA ... SIGH ...
WHAT A CRICKETER.!

TRUE. HOWEVER, I OFTEN WONDER. HE PLAYED IN ONLY TWO
COUNTRIES AND MOST OF HIS CRICKET WAS AGAINST ENGLAND.
HOW WOULD HE HAVE FARED IF HE HAD TO TRAVEL AROUND THE WORLD?

BRADMAN MISSED ONLY ONE OVERSEAS SERIES IN HIS TIME, FOR MEDICAL
REASONS. IT WAS IN SOUTH AFRICA. IN THAT SERIES, JACK FINGLETON
HAMMERED THREE HUNDREDS. BUT FOR THE SOUTH AFRICAN TOUR,
FINGLETON WOULD HAVE AVERAGED 32 IN HIS CAREER. OVERALL
HE AVERAGED 40. NOW JUST THINK WHAT BRADMAN COULD HAVE
MANAGED HAD HE FEASTED ON THOSE BOWLERS.

DURING THAT SAME SEASON, 1935-36, A TEAM OF VERY OLD AUSTRALIAN
STARS VISITED INDIA AND PLAYED FOUR UNOFFICIAL 'TESTS'. MOST
OF THE YOUNGSTERS IN THE SIDE WERE MINOR FIRST-CLASS CRICKETERS.
THEY PLAYED THE FULL-STRENGTH INDIA AND DREW THE 'TEST' SERIES 2-2.
ONE WONDERS WHAT BRADMAN WOULD HAVE DONE IF HE HAD TOURED INDIA.

DURING THE TOUR MACARTNEY WAS 50, RYDER 47,
IRONMONGER 52, OXENHAM 44, HENDRY 40

MEGAN PONSFORD

WHEN ONE SAYS BRADMAN PLAYED MOST OF HIS CRICKET AGAINST ENGLAND AND
TOURED ONLY ENGLAND, IT REALLY MEANS THAT HE PLAYED MOST OF HIS CRICKET
AGAINST THE STRONGEST OPPOSITION OF THAT ERA, AND ONLY TOURED THE
COUNTRY WHICH WAS THEN THE TOUGHEST FOR AN AUSTRALIAN TO TOUR.
WHICH ACTUALLY UNDERLINES THAT HE WAS THE GREATEST BATSMAN EVER.

1950 - 1961
BENT ARMS AND DODGY WICKETS

AFTER THE RETIREMENT OF BRADMAN THERE WAS A SHIFT OF POWER WHICH BEGAN SLOWLY
AND THEN TOOK RAPID PROMINENCE.
AIDED ONCE IN A WHILE BY DODGY WICKETS, ENGLAND DOMINATED MOST OF THE 1950S.
THERE WERE SOME SUPREME BOWLING PERFORMANCES, SUCH AS
THE 19 FOR 90 BY JIM LAKER AT MANCHESTER, 1956 OR
THE FURIOUS DESTRUCTION CARRIED OUT BY FRANK TYSON DURING THE 1954-55 SERIES.

NOW DO YOU KNOW WHAT 19 FOR 90 IS?

I DO.

SOME OF THE HIGHLIGHTS OF THE DECADE ALSO ENDED UP IN LOVE LETTERS.

DAVID FRITH
AND
DEBBIE FRITH

THE PERIOD, HOWEVER, ENDED WITH AUSTRALIA REASSERTING SUPREMACY.
THERE WAS ALSO A PHASE WHEN SUSPECT BOWLING ACTIONS
CLOUDED THE CRICKETING HORIZONS.

WITH THE END OF THE WAR CAME CHANGES - WELFARE STATE, NHS, COMMITMENT TO FULL EMPLOYMENT, MIXED ECONOMY, RECOGNITION OF TRADE UNIONS - AND A STRUGGLING POUND. CLASS DISTINCTIONS WERE DISAPPEARING SLOWLY

EVEN BERTIE WOOSTER WAS SENT PACKING TO RETRAIN HIMSELF FOR A JOB

BUT IN SOME QUARTERS THE CHANGES WERE DIFFICULT TO RING THROUGH... SUCH AS THE AMATEUR-PROFESSIONAL DIVIDE IN CRICKET

AT LEAST WE DON'T HAVE TO CALL THEM MR ANY MORE.

FJ Titmus, should read Titmus, FJ.

THUS, IN 1950-51, IN SPITE OF THERE BEING STALWARTS LIKE HUTTON AND COMPTON IN THE TEAM, IT WAS FREDDIE BROWN, THE VERY FACE OF JOHN BULL, WHO LED MCC TO AUSTRALIA

The Ashes

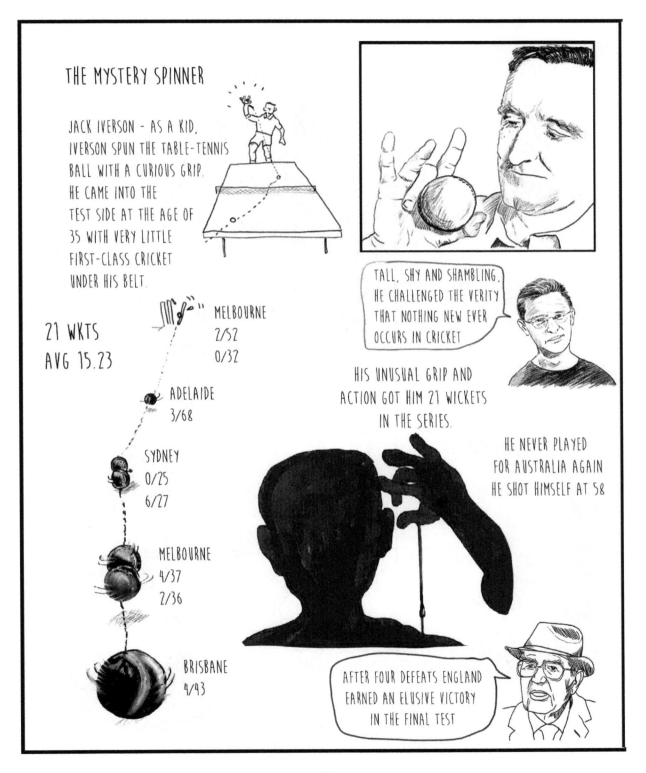

1950-51 FIRST TEST BRISBANE
DAY 1
AUS 228/10
NEIL HARVEY 74
DAY 2
WHAT IS IT WITH YOU? DRAWING DOGS EVERYWHERE!
THIS IS WHEN THE DOG HAD IT'S DAY. BESIDES YOU CAN'T GO MUCH WRONG ADDING A DOG TO A BOOK
DAY 3
ENG 68/7 DEC
AUS 32/7 DEC
ENG 30/6
SWANTON
THIS DAY'S PLAY WILL HAVE IT'S OWN PLACE IN CRICKET HISTORY
DECLARING NOW? BUT SKIPPER I CAME IN AT NO 6 AND AM JUST 6 NOT OUT
DAY 4 HUTTON 62 NOT OUT AFTER COMING IN AT NO 8
ENG 122/10
HUTTON REMINDS ME OF C T STUDD OF 1882
FREDDIE BROWN IS MONKEYING AROUND

IN 1952, WITH INDIA TOURING ENGLAND, THE CAPTAINCY WAS FINALLY HANDED TO A PROFESSIONAL. LEN HUTTON TOOK HIS RIGHTFUL PLACE AT THE HELM.

VIJAY HAZARE

SOME DID NOT LIKE IT THOUGH, WANTING TO SEE THE AMATEUR DAVID SHEPPARD AT THE HELM INSTEAD

BUT IT IS HUTTON WHO'LL BE A KNIGHT. I'LL BE A BISHOP

AM I A JOKE TO YOU?

1953 THE CORONATION YEAR

THE FIRST FOUR TESTS WERE DRAWN, MUCH OF THE STALEMATE ENGINEERED BY TREVOR BAILEY'S PATHOLOGICALLY SLOW BATTING. AT LORD'S BAILEY AND WATSON SAVED ENGLAND WITH A LIMPET-LIKE PARTNERSHIP. AT LEEDS, HE SCORED 38 IN NEARLY FOUR AND A HALF HOURS AND APPEALED FOR LIGHT IN THE MID-DAY SUN TO PREVENT LINDWALL FROM STARTING ANOTHER OVER BEFORE LUNCH. AFTER THAT THE BARNACLE BOWLED DOWN THE LEG TO PREVENT AUSTRALIA FROM GOING FOR A WIN.

MY SHADOW IS JUST A SMALL DOT. THE LIGHT MUST BE POOR

THE TESTS ALSO SAW THE ONLY BONAFIDE SUPERHERO OF OUR COMIC STRIP - DON BRADMAN, MAKING FOR THE PRESSBOX, WHERE HE RAN INTO HIS ETERNAL NEMESIS, DOUGLAS JARDINE

CORONATION YEAR ...
AND THE JEWEL IN THE CROWN WAS LEN HUTTON AND HIS MEN REGAINING THE ASHES AFTER 20 YEARS

THE FINAL TEST SAW FRED TRUEMAN STRIKE SOME QUICK BLOWS.

THIS WAS FOLLOWED BY THE FIRST OF THE MANY WRECKAGES BY THE SURREY SPIN-TWINS JIM LAKER AND TONY LOCK.

ENGLAND REGAINED THE ASHES WHEN DENIS COMPTON HOOKED ARTHUR MORRIS TO THE LEG BOUNDARY

IS THAT THE ASHES? YES, ENGLAND HAVE WON THE ASHES

BRIAN JOHNSTON

THE SCENES FROM THE OVAL TEST WERE REUSED IN THE CLASSIC MOVIE 'THE FINAL TEST'. STARRING JACK WARNER, THIS FEATURED HUTTON, COMPTON, EVANS, BEDSER AND OTHER ENGLISH CRICKETERS IN BIT ROLES.

The Ashes

THAT WAS THE LAST TOUR OF THE GREAT LEN HUTTON. HE MOVED AWAY WITH TREMENDOUS SUCCESS AS A CAPTAIN. QUITE A STATEMENT FOR THE PROFESSIONALS ...

...NOT EVERYONE'S CUP OF TEA

1956

AUSTRALIA LAKERED

AT LORD'S KEITH MILLER'S 10 WICKETS PUT AUSTRALIA ONE UP, IN SPITE OF PETER MAY'S RESISTANCE

IN MAY ENGLAND HAD A NEW CAPTAIN. AMATEUR AGAIN, BUT A DESERVING ONE.

MILLER ALSO SCORED 109 AT LORD'S IN 1953. HE IS THE ONLY PLAYER ON BATTING AND BOWLING HONOURS BOARDS AT LORD'S FOR ASHES PERFORMANCE

HOWEVER, AT LEEDS THE SURREY SPIN-TWINS, LAKER AND LOCK PICKED UP 18 WICKETS TO MAKE IT 1-1

AT MANCHESTER, LAKER DECIDED TO DETACH HIMSELF FROM HIS SPIN TWIN LOCK PICKED UP THE SCALP OF BURKE, THE THIRD WICKET OF THE FIRST INNINGS. OTHER THAN THAT, IT WAS ALL LAKER

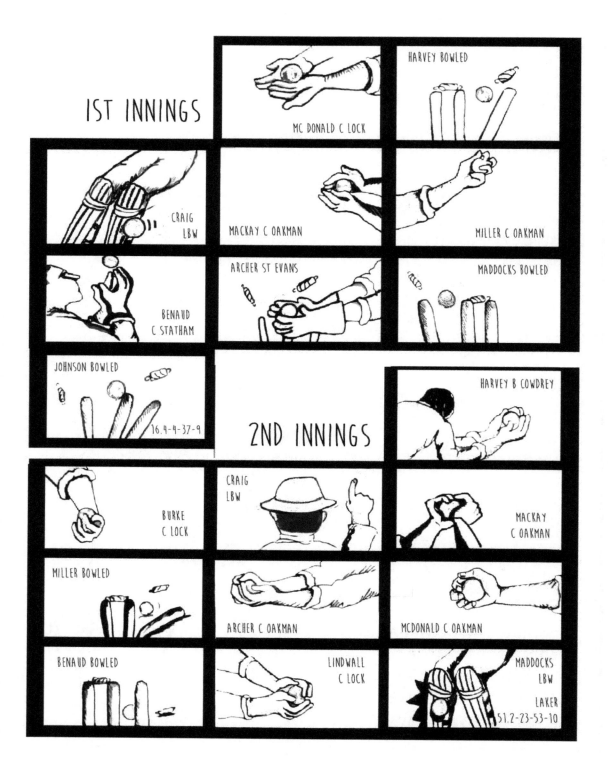

1958-59.

ALL ABOUT BENT ARMS

PETER MAY'S ENGLISHMEN WERE BILLED AS
THE OVERWHELMING FAVOURITES TO WIN THE ASHES.
HOWEVER, PROBLEMS STARTED WAY BEFORE THE TOUR.

SPINNING ACE JIM LAKER FELL OUT WITH CAPTAIN PETER MAY
OVER SOME OF THE LATTER'S COMMENTS FOLLOWING A COUNTY MATCH.

LEFT-ARM SPINNER JOHNNY WARDLE FELL FOUL
OF THE MCC SELECTORS AND LOST HIS PLACE
IN THE SIDE AFTER CONTROVERSIAL GHOST-WRITTEN
NEWSPAPER ARTICLES WERE PUBLISHED UNDER HIS NAME.

CHECK MAY-TE !

AUSTRALIAN SKIPPER RICHIE BENAUD
CONTINUALLY OUT-GENERALLED
MAY WITH HIS INCISIVE STRATEGIES.

BESIDES, IN BENAUD AND ALAN DAVIDSON
AUSTRALIA FOUND THE PLATFORM ON WHICH
THEIR CRICKET WAS TO REST FOR SEVERAL YEARS

LAKER

IT WAS LIKE STANDING IN THE MIDDLE OF A DARTS MATCH.

THE BIGGEST PROBLEM WAS THE CONTROVERSIAL ACTION OF SEVERAL OF THE AUSTRALIAN BOWLERS. IAN MECKIFF, IN PARTICULAR, WAS EXTREMELY SUCCESSFUL IN THE SERIES. BUT CRITICISM OF HIS ACTION WOULD SOON LEAD TO HIS VERY PREMATURE RETIREMENT.

ENGLAND WAS ALSO PLAGUED BY INJURIES.

BESIDES, FORMER ASHES HEROES 'TYPHOON' TYSON AND 'BARNACLE' BAILEY WERE CLEARLY OVER THE HILL.

FINALLY THERE WAS THE DRAG OF SOME OF THE BOWLERS. HAVING A BALL THROWN AT YOU FROM 18 YARDS BLIGHTS THE SUNNIEST DISPOSITION.

LOCK   LOADER

ONLY OUR GUYS WERE NOT TOTALLY CLEAN EITHER.

THE EVENTS OF THE MELBOURNE TEST AT THE NEW YEAR WOULD HAVE TESTED THE PHILOSOPHICAL DETACHMENT OF ANY CRICKET WRITER, OF WHATEVER SCHOOL.

SWANTON, TOO WAS CLEARLY NOT IMPRESSED BY THE 'THROWING'

JACK FINGLETON'S VIEWS ABOUT THE ACTION OF THE BOWLERS WAS CLEAR FROM THE NAME OF THE TOUR BOOK HE PENNED.

IN THE END AUSTRALIA WON 4-0

1950-51   Aus 4 Eng 1
1953   Eng 1 Aus 0
1954-55   Eng 3 Aus 1
1956   Eng 2 Aus 1
1958-59   Aus 4 Eng 0
1961   Aus 2 Eng 1

Cumulative Ashes Head to Head
Tests - Aus 70 Eng 61
Series - Eng 21 Aus 18

ENG   AUS

1961 – 1968
MORE ACTION OFF THE FIELD

THE 1960S SAW CRICKET IN THE DOLDRUMS.
WHILE THE REST OF THE WORLD SAW SWEEPING CHANGES, TEST CRICKET
LANGUISHED INTO DRAB, DRY DRAWS DOMINATING THE SCENES.

OF THE 25 ASHES TESTS CONTESTED IN THE 1960S, ONLY 10 SAW RESULTS.
THE ASHES ALSO REMAINED WITH THE AUSTRALIANS ALL THROUGH.
THE DECADE ENDED WITH ENDLESS CONTROVERSY AROUND BASIL D'OLIVEIRA,
THE CAPE COLOURED CRICKETER WHO REDESIGNED THE CRICKETING,
SPORTING AND POLITICAL LANDSCAPE OF THE WORLD WITH HIS INNINGS OF
158 AT THE OVAL.

ALSO IN THE FACTUAL SENSE THAT
WAS 'ACTUALLY' WHEN CRICKET
CEASED TO BE A GENTLEMEN'S GAME

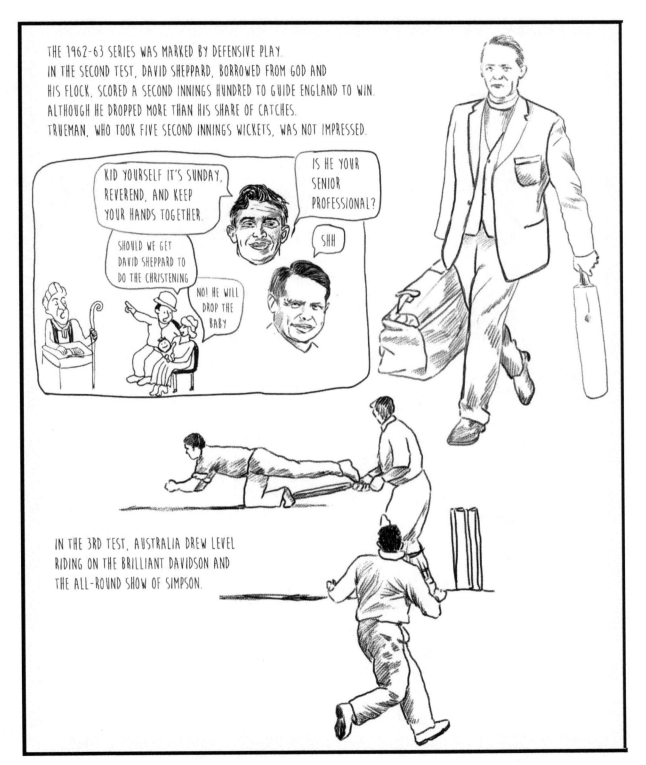

THE 1962-63 SERIES WAS MARKED BY DEFENSIVE PLAY.
IN THE SECOND TEST, DAVID SHEPPARD, BORROWED FROM GOD AND
HIS FLOCK, SCORED A SECOND INNINGS HUNDRED TO GUIDE ENGLAND TO WIN.
ALTHOUGH HE DROPPED MORE THAN HIS SHARE OF CATCHES.
TRUEMAN, WHO TOOK FIVE SECOND INNINGS WICKETS, WAS NOT IMPRESSED.

KID YOURSELF IT'S SUNDAY, REVEREND, AND KEEP YOUR HANDS TOGETHER.

IS HE YOUR SENIOR PROFESSIONAL?

SHH

SHOULD WE GET DAVID SHEPPARD TO DO THE CHRISTENING

NO! HE WILL DROP THE BABY

IN THE 3RD TEST, AUSTRALIA DREW LEVEL
RIDING ON THE BRILLIANT DAVIDSON AND
THE ALL-ROUND SHOW OF SIMPSON.

WITH THE SERIES LEVEL, BOTH SIDES BECAME DEFENSIVE. KEN BARRINGTON, PROMOTED TO NO 3, SCORED A TRUCKLOAD OF RUNS.

SHE'S A LOOKER

THE RESULT WAS SLOW, OFTEN DULL CRICKET.

THE FOCUS WAS MORE ON WHAT CAPTAIN TED DEXTER'S WIFE WAS WEARING

DAVIDSON CALLED IT A DAY AT THE END OF THE SERIES. IN HIS LAST SERIES, HE AND SKIPPER BENAUD COMBINED TO CAPTURE 41 WICKETS.

ENG 1- AUS1

IT IS A SAD BLOW TO CRICKET THAT HARVEY AND DAVIDSON ARE QUITTING THE GAME, BUT ... THEY ARE RETIRING AT THE SAME TIME AS 100,000 SPECTATORS."

RICHIE BENAUD'S 63 WICKETS AS ASHES CAPTAIN IS MORE THAN TWICE THAT OF THE NEXT IN THE LIST, MONTY NOBLE (31) . ALAN DAVIDSON'S 84 WICKETS CAME AT 23.76 APIECE. BOTH WERE HANDY WITH THE BAT AS WELL.

1964 THE FOLLOWING SERIES WAS EVEN MORE FRUSTRATING. AFTER RAIN RUINED THE FIRST TWO TESTS, AUSTRALIA RODE A MAGNIFICENT PETER BURGE ASSAULT ON TRUEMAN TO WIN THE THIRD.

BUT THEN CAPTAIN BOBBY SIMPSON WENT ON AN OVERDRIVE TO MAKE THE ASHES SAFE. HIS 311 AT OLD TRAFFORD WAS DUBBED 'THE MURDER OF CRICKET' BY DAILY MAIL.
WITH BARRINGTON RESPONDING WITH 256, IT WAS A MAMMOTH AND MEANINGLESS RUN-FEAST.

IN HIS 51ST INNINGS, SIMPSON IMPROVED HIS HIGHEST SCORE FROM 92 TO 311. ONLY ASHES CAPTAIN TO SCORE A TRIPLE.
THE NEXT BEST BY AN AUSSIE CAPTAIN IN ENGLAND IS EXACTLY 100 LESS, 211 BY BILLY MURDOCH IN 1884

AT THE OVAL TRUEMAN CAPTURED HIS 300TH WICKET.

ANYONE ELSE GETTING THERE WILL BE BLOODY TIRED.

HAHAHA

1965-66
ENG 1 AUS 1

YET ANOTHER BORING
SERIES ON SLOW WICKETS.
TITMUS AND ALLEN SPUN
ENGLAND TO VICTORY
AT SYDNEY.

AT ADELAIDE LAWRY (119) AND
SIMPSON (225) ADDED 244 AND
HAWKE AND MCKENZIE SKITTLED
ENGLISH WICKETS TO
RESTORE PARITY.

IN THE DECIDER, IT WAS TAKEN TO ANOTHER
RIDICULOUS LEVEL WITH BOB COWPER HITTING
307 OVER 12 HOURS AND 7 MINUTES.

The Ashes

1968.

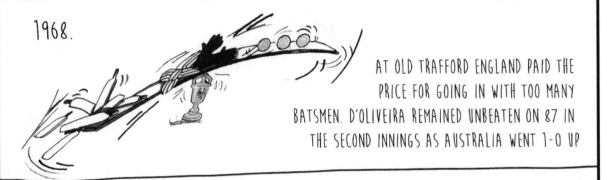

AT OLD TRAFFORD ENGLAND PAID THE PRICE FOR GOING IN WITH TOO MANY BATSMEN. D'OLIVEIRA REMAINED UNBEATEN ON 87 IN THE SECOND INNINGS AS AUSTRALIA WENT 1-0 UP

AT LORD'S CAPTAIN COLIN COWDREY HAD SOME BAD NEWS. D'OLIVEIRA HAD BEEN DROPPED.

ALSO, OTHERS HAD SOME CURIOUS SUGGESTIONS

I KNOW YOU DID VERY WELL AT OLD TRAFFORD AND YOU'RE DISAPPOINTED. BUT BEFORE THE SEASON IS OUT, YOU'LL BE BACK.

WOULD YOU CONSIDER MAKING YOURSELF UNAVAILABLE FOR ENGLAND, BUT LIKELY TO PLAY FOR SOUTH AFRICA IF PERMITTED, DOLLY ?!

AT LORD'S AND EDGBASTON AUSTRALIA WERE SAVED FROM THE THREATS OF SWING AND SPIN BY INCLEMENT WEATHER. AND THERE WAS A STALEMATE AT HEADINGLEY

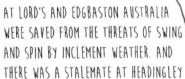

UMBRELLA FIELD OF THIS SORT IS HELPFUL

ALL THE WHILE AGENTS OF THE SOUTH AFRICAN GOVERNMENT TRIED TO BRIBE D'OLIVEIRA TO MAKE HIMSELF UNAVAILABLE FOR THE 1968-69 TOUR.

T. Oosthuizen

£4000 A YEAR, WITH ALL EXPENSES THROWN IN A CAR, A HOUSE. YOU NEED TO BE AVAILABLE IMMEDIATELY FOR THE JOB, AND UNAVAILABLE FOR ENGLAND.

The Ashes

AFTER THE INNINGS COWDREY ASSURED D'OLIVEIRA THAT HIS PLACE IN THE TEAM WAS SECURE.

I WANT YOU IN SOUTH AFRICA. IF ANYONE AT THE TOUR SELECTION MEETING ASKS ME IF I AM PREPARED TO ACCEPT RESPONSIBILITY FOR ANYTHING THAT MIGHT HAPPEN ON THE TOUR SHOULD YOU BE SELECTED, I SHALL SAY I AM PREPARED TO DO SO.

BUT WHEN THE SELECTION COMMITTEE MET, D'OLIVEIRA'S NAME WAS CAREFULLY IGNORED. THE SELECTORS INSISTED THAT THE TEAM WAS PICKED ON CRICKETING MERIT. FEW BELIEVED THAT.

THE PRESS WAS SCATHING IN THEIR DENOUNCEMENT OF THE OMISSION

THE GUARDIAN

Any who would swallow that would believe the moon was a currant bun.

Daily Mirror

In the bad old days the colour of your tie was of paramount importance. Now the colour of the skin seems to transcend all logical and sporting concerns.

TO SAY HE IS NOT IN THE BEST 16 CRICKETERS OF ENGLAND IS NONSENSE. I AM CONVINCED THAT IF DOLLY WAS WHITE HE WOULD BE PACKING HIS BAGS

CONSTANTINE

HOWEVER, WARWICKSHIRE MEDIUM PACER TOM CARTWRIGHT WITHDREW BECAUSE OF SHOULDER INJURY. D'OLIVEIRA WAS SELECTED IN HIS PLACE.

TOM WITHDREW FOR THREE REASONS: HIS INJURY, THE EFFECT ON HIS FAMILY OF BEING AWAY ALL WINTER AND HIS UNEASE AT THE REACTION OF THE SOUTH AFRICAN PARLIAMENT WHEN BASIL D'OLIVEIRA WAS NOT SELECTED. THESE COMBINED TO MAKE HIM THINK, 'I JUST DON'T WANT TO GO'.

STEPHEN CHALKE

SOUTH AFRICAN PRIME MINISTER BJ VORSTER WOULD NOT AGREE TO A COLOURED CRICKETER PLAYING WITH WHITE CRICKETERS IN SOUTH AFRICA. THE TOUR WAS CANCELLED.

THE MCC TEAM AS CONSTITUTED NOW IS NOT THE TEAM OF MCC BUT THE TEAM OF THE ANTI-APARTHEID MOVEMENT

THE MCC STILL TRIED TO GET SOUTH AFRICA OVER FOR A TOUR IN 1970. THAT LED TO THE STOP THE SEVENTY TOUR MOVEMENT THAT SHOOK THE ESTABLISHMENT. IT DISRUPTED THE SPRINGBOK RUGBY TOUR IN 1969-70 AND EVENTUALLY SAW THE 1970 VISIT CANCELLED AS WELL.

STOP THE SEVENTY TOUR

SOUTH AFRICA WOULD PLAY TEST CRICKET ONCE AGAIN IN 1991.

1962–63 Aus 1 Eng 1
1964   Aus 1 Eng 0
1965–66 Aus 1 Eng 1
1968   Eng 1 Aus 1

Cumulative Ashes Head to Head
Tests - Aus 74 Eng 64
Series - Eng 21 Aus 19

ENG

AUS

1970-71 - 1978-79
DECADE OF SWEEPING CHANGES

THE NEW DECADE SAW A DRASTIC CHANGE FROM THE DRAB, OFTEN BLAND, ASHES OF THE 1960S.
JOHN SNOW BREATHED FIRE IN 1970-71, AND THE AUSTRALIANS PERFECTED THEIR ANSWER ...
NOT ONLY TO SNOW BUT PERHAPS TO THE BODYLINE MAYHEM OF 1932-33 ...
IN 1974-75 WITH DENNIS LILLEE AND JEFF THOMSON HERALDING AN ERA OF BRUTAL,
UNCOMPROMISING TEST CRICKET.

AT THE SAME TIME CHANGES WERE ON THEIR WAY.

ONE DAY CRICKET EVOLVED QUICKLY AND THE FIRST EVER WORLD CUP WAS HELD IN 1975.

(TECHNICALLY THOUGH, THE FIRST
EVER WORLD CUP WAS IN 1973
IN THE WOMEN'S GAME)

AND IN 1977, MEDIA MOGUL KERRY PACKER SHOOK THE WORLD BY CREATING A PARALLEL
CIRCUIT OF THE GAME WHICH DRAINED THE BEST OF EXISTING CRICKETING TALENT AWAY
FROM THE TRADITIONAL CONTESTS.
CRICKET WAS SOON TO BE REVOLUTIONISED, ENTERING A ZONE OF PROFESSIONALISM,
COMMERCIALISATION AND TELEVISING AS NEVER BEFORE.

THERE WERE SOME HIGHLIGHTS FOR AUSTRALIA, SUCH AS GREG CHAPPELL MAKING A CENTURY ON DEBUT. IT ALSO SAW DENNIS LILLEE AND ROD MARSH ENTERING INTERNATIONAL CRICKET.

MY GLOVES SEEM METALLIC

HOWEVER, THE TEAM WAS COMPROMISED BY WEIRD SELECTION PROCESS.

WELL PLAYED BILL AND YES, YOU'RE NO LONGER THE CAPTAIN ... AND NOT IN THE TEAM EITHER.

AUSTRALIA 116
LAWRY 60*
ENG 2 AUS 0

YOU MUST BE KIDDING, MR SELECTOR.

CAPTAIN'S LOG
I.R.
WE WILL BE DELIGHTED NOT TO BOWL AT LAWRY.

AFTER THE THIRD TEST MATCH AT MELBOURNE WAS CANCELLED, TWO STRIKING EVENTS TOOK PLACE. AN UNPRECEDENTED 7TH TEST WAS ADDED TO THE SCHEDULE TO MAKE UP FOR THE LOST GAME.

WHAT HAPPENS TO THE NIGHTWATCHMAN?

AND THE FIRST EVER ONE DAY INTERNATIONAL WAS WITNESSED WHEN RAIN WASHED OFF THE TEST AT MELBOURNE

DON BRADMAN

THE VICTORIOUS ENGLAND SIDE RECORDED THE ASHES SONG AS — ACCORDING TO DAVID FRITH — THE PERMANENT IF UNMELODIC SOUVENIR OF A HISTORIC WIN.

AT TRENT BRIDGE, A FIGHTING PARTNERSHIP BETWEEN TONY GREIG AND BASIL D'OLIVEIRA SAVED ENGLAND FROM DEFEAT.

TOO MANY SOUTH AFRICANS GET BOSS ON IT, MUST BE AN ANC PLOT

AT LEEDS, ON A FUSARIUM AFFECTED WICKET, DEREK UNDERWOOD BOWLED ENGLAND TO VICTORY.

IN 1935, LEATHER JACKETS HAD DESTROYED THE LORD'S PITCH AND IT HAD SEEN XENOPHON BALASKAS BOWLING SOUTH AFRICA TO A WIN.

IAN CHAPPELL

MICK JAGGER

I WENT TO SEE ENGLAND, BUT ENGLAND LOST.

THERE WERE INTERESTING VISITORS IN THE AUSTRALIAN DRESSING ROOM.

AT THE OVAL THE CHAPPELL BROTHERS GOT HUNDREDS. AND THERE ROSE THE MENACE OF DENNIS LILLEE.

FOR THE FIRST TIME NO ONE FROM NEW SOUTH WALES WAS IN THE AUSTRALIAN TEAM

LILLEE WOULD PLAGUE ENGLAND FOR LONG.

AND THE CHAPPELLS WOULD NOT BE THE LAST IN THE BAND OF BROTHERS TO PLAGUE ENGLAND.

THE CHAPPELLS WERE THE FIRST PAIR OF BROTHERS TO GET HUNDREDS IN THE SAME TEST INNINGS

MARK AND STEVE WAUGH.

SHAUN AND MITCHELL MARSH

The Ashes

1974-75

DENNIS LILLEE
AND JEFF THOMSON
BLEW ENGLAND
AWAY IN 1974-75.

THEY WERE BATTERED BLACK AND BLUE.
AT BRISBANE, PERTH, ADELAIDE AND SYDNEY
THE ENGLISHMEN WERE DECIMATED

LILLIAN THOMSON'S BOWLING BASED ON RALPH STEADMAN'S DRAWING OF DENNIS LILLEE'S BOWLING AND THE APPEAL THEREAFTER

EVERY MORNING ON THE RADIO, THE NEWS COMES FROM AUSTRALIA
THE ENGLISH BATSMEN ONCE AGAIN HAVE HAD A GHASTLY FAILURE.

LILLIAN THOMSON'S BOWLING ONCE AGAIN CAUSED THE COLLAPSE
I ALWAYS THOUGHT TEST CRICKET WAS INTENDED JUST FOR CHAPS.

LILLIAN THOMSON IS AUSTRALIA'S FINEST FLOWER
MAIDEN BOWLING OVERS AT 100 MILES AN HOUR

SHE'S THE FASTEST LADY BOWLER THE WORLD HAS EVER SEEN
HER BUMPERS AWE INSPIRING HER LANGUAGE FAR FROM CLEAN

RICHARD STILGOE

237

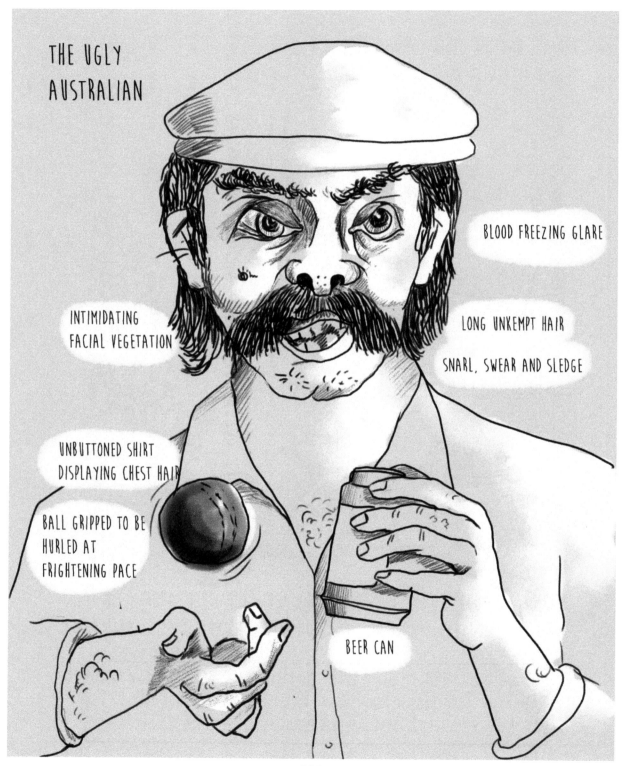

The Ashes

IN 1976-77 THE SIDES PLAYED A
GREAT TEST MATCH AT THE MCG
TO COMMEMORATE 100 YEARS OF
TEST CRICKET. IT ENDED WITH
THE EXACT SAME RESULT AS
THE INAUGURAL TEST
MATCH IN 1876-77.
THIS IS NOT COUNTED
AMONG THE ASHES

AUSTRALIA WON BY 45 RUNS AS A
GLITTERATI OF PAST ASHES STARS
WATCHED FROM THE SIDELINES.

THE TWO GROUPS OF CRICKETERS WERE ENEMY FACTIONS. HOWEVER, WHEN THEY CHANCED UPON EACH OTHER AT THE SYDNEY AIRPORT, CAMARADERIE RULED.

IT WOULD ALL BE MUCH EASIER IF THE ADMINISTRATORS COULD COMMUNICATE LIKE THIS.

BARRY RICHARDS

THE PACKER SUPERTESTS AND INTERCONTINENTAL CUP ONE DAY MATCHES RAN PARALLEL TO THE TEST SERIES, ... AND THE CRICKET ON VIEW WAS WAY SUPERIOR IN THE UNOFFICIAL VERSION OF THE GAME

HOWEVER, THE TRADITIONAL TEST MATCHES DID SEE THE NOVELTY OF 7 ENGLISH CRICKETERS DONNING HELMETS IN THE OPENING TEST

BIG BOYS PLAY AT NIGHT

THE NIGHT-WATCHMAN SURE WORKS LATE HOURS HERE.

TEST CRICKET IN PRISTINE WHITE

THAT'S WHY THEY DID NOT SIGN UP FOR PACKER. THEY DID NOT LOSE THEIR HEADS.

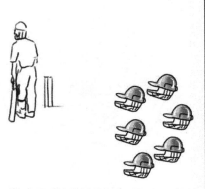

THE FACELESS AUSTRALIAN SIDE BOASTED ONLY KIM HUGHES AND RODNEY HOGG AS WORLD CLASS PLAYERS. THEY WERE EASILY OUTCLASSED BY THE COMPARATIVELY STAR-STUDDED ENGLISHMEN.

ENG 5 AUS 1

DAVID GOWER GOT 402 RUNS IN A RELATIVELY LOW-SCORING SERIES

DEAR MIKE,
ON BEHALF OF THE WSC I'D LIKE TO PUT TO YOU A CHALLENGE MATCH AGAINST IAN CHAPPELL'S AUSTRALIANS FOR A $50,000 PURSE.
YOURS SINCERELY,
KERRY PACKER

DEAR KERRY,
I THINK YOU'LL APPRECIATE THAT ANY MATCH WE PLAY ON THIS TOUR HAS TO BE ARRANGED WITH THE TCCB. WE ARE INVOLVED WITH TESTS AND ODIS RIGHT UP TO 17 FEB, ON WHICH DAY WE LEAVE AUSTRALIA.
YOURS SINCERELY,
MIKE BREARLEY.

PACKER EVEN BAITED BREARLEY, TRYING TO PIT THE WSC AUSTRALIANS AGAINST THE VISITING ENGLISHMEN. BUT THE ASTUTE SKIPPER DID NOT BITE.

BUT THE TWO SEASONS OF PACKER CHANGED CRICKET COMPLETELY, MOST OF IT FOR THE BETTER.

I LIKE THE CRICKET ... NOW THAT THEY COME IN SO MANY COLOURS.

HE WAS DEFINITELY OUT. I SAW THE ACTION REPLAY ON CHANNEL 9... IN SLOW MOTION.

1970-71   Eng 2 Aus 0
1972   Eng 2 Aus 2
1974-75   Aus 4 Eng 1
1975   Aus 1 Eng 0
1976-77 (Centenary, non-Ashes) Aus
1977   Eng 3 Aus 0
1978-79   Eng 5 Aus 1
1979-80 (Non-Ashes) Aus 3 Eng 0
1980   (Centenary non-Ashes) draw

Cumulative Ashes Head to Head
Tests - Aus 82 Eng 77
Series - Eng 24 Aus 21

ENG

AUS

IT'S SAD TO SEE CRICKETERS BECOMING INCREASINGLY COMMERCIAL WITH TIMES. I GUESS PACKER IS TO BLAME.

TOM, HAVEN'T YOU BEEN LISTENING? IT WAS ALWAYS ABOUT THE MONEY. I DON'T SEE ANYTHING WRONG WITH THAT. RIGHT FROM THE OUTSET OF ANGLO-AUSTRALIAN CRICKET TALENTED SPORTSMEN WANTED TO EARN MONEY BY ENTERTAINING THE PUBLIC. HOW ELSE WOULD THEY SURVIVE?

INDEED, CRICKETERS WERE VERY POORLY PAID UNTIL THEN. MANY POTENTIALLY GREAT CAREER WERE NIPPED IN THE BUD DUE TO FINANCIAL CONSTRAINTS. PACKER CHANGED ALL THAT. THE LUCRATIVE DEALS CRICKETERS ENJOY NOW HAVE MUCH TO DO WITH THE REVOLUTION HE BROUGHT IN.

PACKER ALSO TRANSFORMED THE EXPERIENCE OF WATCHING CRICKET FOREVER

AS FAR AS THE AUSTRALIANS WERE CONCERNED, THE BOARD WAS NOT WILLING TO RAISE THEIR PAY EVEN AFTER YEARS OF DISCUSSIONS. I'M SURE YOU'VE HEARD IAN CHAPPELL TALK ABOUT IT

FINALLY SPORTSMEN HAVE A BRIEF WINDOW IN THEIR LIFETIME IN WHICH TO EARN THEIR MONEY. THEY ARE NOT LIKE EVERYDAY PROFESSIONALS WORKING TILL 65. IT WAS A BLESSING THAT MONEY CAME INTO THE GAME IN A BIG WAY.

COWPER, FOR EXAMPLE, PLAYED HIS FINAL TEST AT THE AGE OF 27 ... BECAUSE HE HAD TO CONCENTRATE ON HIS PROFESSIONAL CAREER.

1980 - 1987
PROTAGONISTS BECOME SIDE CHARACTERS

THE 1980S STARTED WITH A BANG, WITH THE GREAT IAN BOTHAM SHOW IN THE 1981 ASHES.

HOWEVER, SOON THE CONTEST PETERED OUT INTO A TUSSLE BETWEEN TWO MEDIOCRE SIDES IN THE CONTEXT OF INTERNATIONAL CRICKET - ESPECIALLY WITH WEST INDIES WINNING EVERYTHING IN SIGHT.

WITH THE PAKISTANIS GROWING IN STATURE, THE NEW ZEALANDERS AND THE INDIANS BECOMING FORCES TO RECKON WITH, THE TWO ANCIENT RIVALS HAD BY NOW BECOME RATHER PEDESTRIAN OUTFITS.

WITH THE DEPARTURE OF GREG CHAPPELL, DENNIS LILLEE AND RODNEY MARSH, THE AUSTRALIANS WENT INTO A PHASE OF REBUIDLING IN THE MID-1980S. ENGLAND, SUFFERING SEVERAL BLACKWASHES TO WEST INDIES, AND SOUNDLY BEATEN BY PAKISTAN, INDIA AND NEW ZEALAND, STILL MANAGED TO WIN AT HOME AND IN AUSTRALIA.

IN SHORT, THE GREAT BATTLES HAD BY NOW BECOME A SIDESHOW FOR THE REST OF THE WORLD, ALMOST A SKIRMISH FOR THE WOODEN SPOON

THERE FOLLOWED A FEW TEST MATCHES WHICH WERE NOT CONSIDERED ASHES.

IN 1979-80, WITH TRUCE BETWEEN AUSTRALIAN CRICKET BOARD AND PACKER'S WORLD SERIES CRICKET, THE AUTHORITIES SOUGHT TO RESTORE BALANCE. AUSTRALIA PLAYED TWO TEST SERIES, AGAINST ENGLAND AND THE WEST INDIES, ALTERNATING BETWEEN OPPONENTS. BACK TO FULL-STRENGTH, AUSTRALIA TROUNCED ENGLAND 3-0.

AT PERTH, LILLEE MADE HEADLINES WALKING OUT WITH AN ALUMINIUM BAT.

ANY BOY LOOKING AT THE LILLEE SPECTACLE MUST HAVE THOUGHT IT WAS ALL AN ACCEPTABLE PART OF THE SHOWBIZ INTO WHICH CRICKET IS BEING TRANSFORMED.

IN 1980, THERE WAS A RATHER FORGETTABLE CENTENARY TEST TO COMMEMORATE THE FIRST EVER TEST IN ENGLAND. A DREARY DRAW. THERE WAS AN ASSEMBLY OF ASHES STARS FOR THIS MATCH AS WELL.

THAT TEST SAW THE RETIREMENT OF A LEGEND. IT WAS THE LAST TIME THAT CRICKET LOVERS HEARD JOHN ARLOTT.

28 BOYCOTT, 15 GOWER, 69 FOR 2 — AND AFTER TREVOR BAILEY IT WILL BE CHRISTOPHER MARTIN-JENKINS ...

WHAT CAN ONE SAY IN SUCH CIRCUMSTANCES?

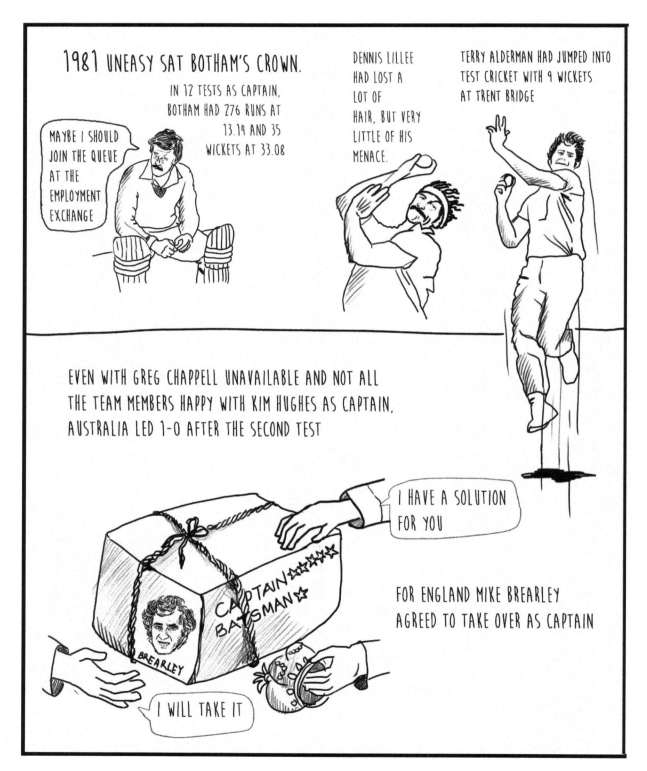

AT LEEDS A RELIEVED BOTHAM TOOK 6/95 AND SCORED 50 IN THE FIRST INNINGS. BUT ENGLAND FOLLOWED ON 227 RUNS BEHIND AND WERE 135 FOR 7 IN THE SECOND INNINGS

ON THE LONELY ROAD I'M TRAVELLING ON. THE ROAD THAT LEADS NOWHERE.

TILL HE GOT TO LEEDS

THE ODDS AGAINST ENGLAND WERE STACKED AT 500-1, ENTICING MARSH AND LILLEE TO A SMALL PUNT EACH

A TANNER EACH WILL BE HARMLESS

A FLUTTER, MATE? AFTER ALL, IN THE FUTURE AUSTRALIA WILL BE LED BY A PUNTER.

The Ashes

BOTHAM ESSAYED 149, ONE OF THE
GREATEST INNINGS UNDER PRESSURE.
AUSTRALIA WERE SET 130 TO WIN.

BOB WILLIS CAPTURED 8/43 TO
DISMISS THE TOURISTS FOR 111

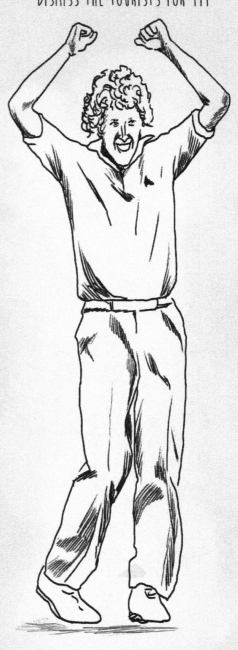

KARTIKEYA DATE

I WONDER WHAT BREARLEY'S CAPTAINCY HAD TO DO WITH BOTHAM PLAYING A MIRACLE INNINGS

FOR THE ENGLISH FAN, THIS MIRACULOUS WIN HAS REPLACED THE DISCOVERY OF WHEEL, FIRE, CAVE PAINTING, MUSIC, GRAVITY, PENICILLIN ETC AS THE GREATEST FEAT OF MANKIND.

WHY NOT? OF COURSE IT IS. BRITAIN WAS IN AGONY AS A SOCIETY IN 1981, THREE MILLION UNEMPLOYED, WIDESPREAD RIOTS, HIGH INFLATION, HIGH INTEREST RATES. A REAL FINAL REALISATION THAT THE DAYS OF GREATNESS HAD WELL TRULY VANISHED, A SAD REALITY FOR A ONCE PROUD COUNTRY, THE LAUGHING STOCK OF THE EUROPEAN COMMUNITY IT HAD JOINED LESS THAN A DECADE BEFORE, WITH LESS THAN FULL APPROVAL EITHER FROM JOINER OR JOINEE. IT WAS A RARE BRIGHT SPOT IN A TIME OF GREAT GLOOM.

WELL SAID

LADBROKES
C MARSH
B LILLEE

WE'RE IN THE MONEY

AND IN THE SOUP

BOTHAM BECAME THE SECOND CRICKETER TO SCORE
A HUNDRED AND TAKE A FIVE-WICKET HAUL IN AN ASHES TEST.
THE ONLY OTHER WAS JACK GREGORY AT MCG IN 1920

1982-83 THE SOUTH AFRICAN CROSS-CONNECTIONS

GRAHAM GOOCH HAD LED AN ENGLISH SIDE TO APARTHEID SOUTH AFRICA ON A REBEL TOUR.
AS A RESULT HE WAS BANNED. GEOFF BOYCOTT, WHO HAD BEEN PART OF THE TEAM, WAS ALSO BANNED
AND DID NOT PLAY TEST CRICKET AGAIN.

ENGLAND WITHOUT GOOCH WAS LIKE TONIC WITHOUT GIN. BUT ENGLAND WITHOUT BOYCOTT WAS LIKE GIN AND TONIC WITHOUT THE GLASS.

ROBIN MARLAR

WE GENERALLY MIGRATE NORTH.

LOTS OF SOUTH AFRICANS ARE ALREADY PLAYING FOR ENGLAND.

WITH GREG CHAPPELL BACK AT THE HELM, AND BACK IN FORM AFTER A SPATE OF ZEROES THE PREVIOUS SEASON, THE AUSTRALIANS WERE SOON TWO UP IN THE SERIES

HOWEVER, SOUTH AFRICAN CONNECTIONS DID NOT ONLY RESULT IN OMISSIONS. KEPLER WESSELS MADE HIS DEBUT FOR AUSTRALIA IN THE SECOND TEST AT BRISBANE, HITTING 162.

THE DUCKS ARE BEHIND ME

VICTORY DID COME AT A PRICE. DURING THE RIOTOUS FIELD INVASION IN THE FIRST TEST, TERRY ALDERMAN TACKLED AN INTRUDER AND DISLOCATED HIS SHOULDER IN THE PROCESS.

A POOR UMPIRING DECISION INVOLVING A RUN-OUT, HOWEVER, HAD MUCH TO DO WITH THE FINAL RESULT OF THE SERIES.

THE AUSTRALIAN
'In or out' riddle opens Ashes decider

AUS 2 ENG 1

WHAT'S THE POINT OF ALL THIS TECHNOLOGY IF WE CANNOT USE IT? WRONG DECISIONS NEED TO BE OVERTURNED BY TELEVISION.

SO NOW YOU NEED FANCY TELEVISION CAMERAS.

THERE WERE SOME SIDE SHOWS DURING THE ONE DAY INTERNATIONALS.
IN THE ONE DAY INTERNATIONAL AT BRISBANE, A PIG WAS RELEASED INTO THE GROUND. ON ONE SIDE WAS WRITTEN 'BOTHAM', ON THE OTHER 'EDDIE'; TARGETING BOTHAM AND HEMMINGS, TWO ENGLISH CRICKETERS WITH NOT EXACTLY THE MOST SVELTE OF PROPORTIONS

THEY SHOULD HAVE USED A BERKSHIRE SOW

SIGH. IF ONLY PIGS HAD WINGS. IT WOULD HAVE BEEN SOMETHING FRESH, BUT THE AQIS WOULD HAVE MADE HEAVY WEATHER.

MUST HAVE BEEN PARSLOE

IN THESE MODERN TIMES EVERY TRAMP WANTS TO BE IN THE LIMELIGHT

DURING THE BENSON AND HEDGES WORLD SERIES ODI BETWEEN ENGLAND AND NEW ZEALAND AT ADELAIDE, FRANCO DOMINIC PRINCI, DRESSED AS CHARLIE CHAPLIN, APPEARED AT THE GROUND AND PROCEEDED TO TAKE GUARD WITH HIS CANE.

JUST AS YOU HAVE JOINED THE GOLD RUSH

1985

♪ BYE BYE BOYCOTT ♪♪

ALTHOUGH THE CRICKET WAS LUKEWARM, THERE WERE INTERESTING SIDELIGHTS. THE SERIES WAS WON 3-1 BY ENGLAND

AT LEEDS, TIM ROBINSON'S 175 DELIGHTED THE SIDE FOR SPECIAL REASONS.

I'm in CHARGE

HOWEVER, ENGLAND HAD THEIR OWN PROBLEMS AFTER ANOTHER WINDIES BLACKWASH AND HUMILIATION AGAINST INDIA, THE CAPTAINCY WAS PASSED ON FROM DAVID GOWER TO MIKE GATTING WITH MINIMUM TACT.

CHAIRMAN OF SELECTORS PETER MAY HAD DONE AS MUCH FOR THE ART OF COMMUNICATION AS BENSON AND HEDGES HAVE DONE FOR PUBLIC HEALTH.

FRANCES EDMONDS

1981   Eng 3 Aus 1
1982–83 Aus 2 Eng 1
1985   Eng 3 Aus 1
1986–87 Eng 2 Aus 1
1987 (bicentennial, non–Ashes) draw

Cumulative Ashes Head to Head
Tests - Aus 87 Eng 86
Series- Eng 27 Aus 22

ENG   AUS

THAT IS THE LAST TIME ENGLAND WOULD SMILE IN ANOTHER 18 YEARS.

DURING THE NEXT COUPLE OF DECADES AUSTRALIA WOULD HAMMER ENGLAND EVERYWHERE.

I KNOW.
I GREW UP DURING THOSE YEARS.

THERE'S REALLY NOT MUCH TO WRITE ABOUT THESE YEARS

1989 - 2003
ONE SIDED SHOWS

BY THE TIME THE AUSTRALIANS TRAVELLED TO ENGLAND IN 1989,
THEY HAD BEEN CHISELLED INTO A SUPERB UNIT.

THE COACHING REVOLUTION HAD A BIG ROLE TO PLAY.
A RADICAL IDEA FOR A HYBRID CRICKET GAME FOR SCHOOLCHILDREN,
ALONG WITH THE FORMATION OF A FINISHING SCHOOL FOR
CRICKETERS IN ADELAIDE HELPED CHANGE PERCEPTIONS

BOBBY SIMPSON, WHO AT THE AGE OF 41 HAD COME BACK
TO LEAD AUSTRALIA DURING THE FIRST PACKER YEAR,
NOW PLAYED A STELLAR ROLE AS COACH.

AND CAPTAIN ALLAN BORDER SHEPHERDED THE YOUNG SIDE.
THE WORLD CUP TRIUMPH IN 1987 WAS THE START OF IT ALL

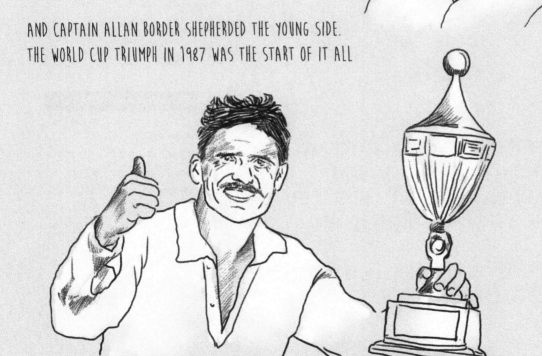

AS ENGLAND SUFFERED FROM AGEING, AND EVENTUALLY RETIRING, STALWARTS, THE AUSTRALIANS KEPT PRODUCING ONE HERO AFTER ANOTHER.

BY THE MID-1990S, AUSTRALIA WAS THE BEST SIDE OF THE WORLD AND ENGLAND HAD SLIPPED TO THE BOTTOM OF THE TEST TABLES.
THEY EVEN MADE A BIG DEAL OF A DRAW AGAINST ZIMBABWE WITH THE SCORES LEVEL.

WE FLIPPIN' MURDERED THEM'

THERE WERE EIGHT CONSECUTIVE SERIES FROM 1989 TO 2003-04 WON BY AUSTRALIA, EQUALLING A RECORD SET BY ENGLAND IN THE EARLY DAYS BETWEEN 1882-83 AND 1890.

THIS WAS THE MOST DISMAL TIME TO BE AN ENGLAND FAN

The Wisden Table				
	P	W	D	L
Australia	14	11	2	1
West Indies	14	7	4	3
South Africa	15	9	1	5
Pakistan	14	6	3	5
India	15	5	3	7
Sri Lanka	16	4	5	7
Zimbabwe	10	2	3	5
New Zealand	16	4	3	9
England	14	3	2	9

CRICKET CONTINUED TO DOMINATE THE NON-CRICKETING HEADLINES AS WE MOVED INTO THE 1990S

To Nelson Mandela in recognition of a great unfinished innings

Don Bradman

IT IS RATHER LIKE SENDING YOUR OPENING BATSMEN TO THE CREASE, ONLY FOR THEM TO FIND, AS THE FIRST BALLS ARE BEING BOWLED, THAT THEIR BATS HAVE BEEN BROKEN BEFORE THE GAME BY THE TEAM CAPTAIN.

PHOENIX RISING - 1989

THE AUSTRALIAN SIDE, VERY MUCH THE UNDERDOGS, CRUSHED ENGLAND 4-0 IT WAS A VICTORY TO CHERISH FOR THE MAN WHO HAD ENGINEERED THE TURNAROUND — ALLAN BORDER.

FOR TERRY ALDERMAN IT WAS REVISITING HAPPY HUNTING GROUNDS, AS HE CAPTURED 41 WICKETS.

THIS IS GRAHAM GOOCH. I'M NOT HERE RIGHT NOW. I'M PROBABLY OUT . . . LBW, TO TERRY ALDERMAN

IN BATTING THE HERO WAS MARK TAYLOR WITH 839 RUNS. NO ONE HAS EVER SCORED THESE MANY RUNS IN A SERIES APART FROM DON BRADMAN (1930) AND WALLY HAMMOND (1928-29).

ALONG WITH GEOFF MARSH, TAYLOR BATTED THROUGH THE ENTIRE FIRST DAY OF THE TRENT BRIDGE TEST, EVENTUALLY PUTTING TOGETHER 329

IAN BOTHAM (62 RUNS AT 15.50 AND 3 WICKETS AT 80.33 IN THE SERIES) PLAYED HIS FINAL ASHES TEST.

IN THE 20TH CENTURY BOTHAM AND LILLEE HAVE TAKEN MORE ASHES WICKETS THAN ANYONE ELSE — BOTH ACCOUNTING FOR 128 BATSMEN

CELEBRATION HAD, HOWEVER, STARTED EARLY FOR THE AUSTRALIANS.
AS THE TEAM FLEW FROM SYDNEY TO LONDON, DAVID BOON CONSUMED A
RECORD 52 CANS OF BEER. IT DROWNED THE PREVIOUS MARK OF 44 HELD
JOINTLY BY ROD MARSH AND DOUG WALTERS, SET IN 1973 ON THEIR
WAY BACK FROM WEST INDIES.

BRIEF STATS: TOTAL CANS: 52

CAN CONTENT: 375-ML

AMOUNT OF BEER: 19.5 LITRES

ALCOHOL CONSUMED: 897 ML (GOING BY 4.6% ABV)

BY THE END OF THE 1989 SUMMER THE FOLLOWING POPPED
UP ON THE WALL OF A SOUTH LONDON UNDERPASS

TIGER MOTH TO THE FLAME — 1990-91

THIS SERIES SAW THE EMERGENCE OF MARK WAUGH WHO SCORED A CENTURY ON DEBUT AT ADELAIDE.

I HOPE THEY ARE NOT TRIPLETS.

BRUCE REID IN PARTICULAR, DESTROYED ENGLAND. THE PACE ATTACK OF REID, CRAIG MCDERMOTT, TERRY ALDERMAN AND MERV HUGHES MANAGED 76 WICKETS BETWEEN THEM.

BESIDES, THE BEDRAGGLED ENGLISH SIDE HAD THEIR OWN PROBLEMS. SUCH AS DAVID GOWER AND JOHN MORRIS HOVERING ABOVE THE GROUND IN A TIGER MOTH DURING A TOUR MATCH.

£27 FOR THE FLIGHT AND £1000 FINE. TOO EXPENSIVE FOR A SHORT HOP OF A JOYRIDE.

1993 - BIZARRE GEOMETRY OF IT ALL

IN 1993 THE STORY OF AUSTRALIAN DOMINANCE CONTINUED, UNDERLINED BY THE FIRST BALL IN ENGLAND SENT DOWN BY SHANE WARNE, WHICH TRAVERSED THE ENTIRE GIRTH OF MIKE GATTING TO BOWL HIM.

GATTING STOOD DUMBFOUNDED, WONDERING AT THE BIZARRE GEOMETRY OF IT ALL... THIS BALL WILL LIVE FOREVER, AS MUCH FOR ITS VERY NATURE AS ITS UNIQUENESS.

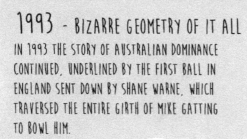

THE BALL OF THE CENTURY' TOOK THE FOCUS AWAY FROM A GRAHAM GOOCH HANDLING THE BALL DISMISSAL IN THE SECOND INNINGS

DAVID SQUIRES

WE ALL BELONG TO BISCUITS

HE HADN'T GOT IT THAT WRONG SINCE HE WENT ON A SANCTIONS-BUSTING TOUR OF APARTHEID ERA SOUTH AFRICA

THERE WAS MORE CONFOUNDING GEOMETRY.- WARNE'S 34 WICKETS STOOD ON SOME SOLID, IF PAUNCHY, PLATFORM. MERV HUGHES CAPTURED 31 WICKETS AND DAVID BOON BLASTED 555 RUNS IN A CELEBRATION OF MASS AND MOUSTACHE

REALLY? YOU HAD TO STEP DOWN NOW? AUSTRALIA ON RAMPAGE, AND WITHIN HOURS OF THE ANNOUNCEMENT THE PRESS HAS FOUND OUT WHERE I LIVE AND ALL ABOUT MY GIRLFRIEND.

SIZE AND MOUSTACHE PROVED LUCKY FOR GRAHAM GOOCH AS WELL, WHO ENDED THE MOST SUCCESSFUL ENGLISH BATSMAN. HOWEVER, WHEN THE SERIES STOOD 3-0 FOR AUSTRALIA AFTER THE HEADINGLEY TEST, IT WAS THE SAD END TO HIS REIGN AS ENGLAND CAPTAIN. CHAIRMAN OF SELECTORS TED DEXTER ALSO RESIGNED BEFORE THE START OF THE NEXT TEST MATCH

AFTER LOSING THE FIRST TEST AS CAPTAIN, ATHERTON LED HIS TEAM TO A CONSOLATION WIN AT THE OVAL, MAINLY DUE TO THE BOWLING OF ANGUS FRASER.

MAYBE THE AUSTRALIANS WERE TIRED, MAYBE VENUS WAS IN THE RIGHT JUXTAPOSITION WITH MARS.

MAK PATAUDI OFFICIATED AS THE MATCH REFEREE IN THE FIRST TWO TESTS OF THE 1993 ASHES. AFTER HIS FATHER, HE ALSO GOT INTO AN OFFICIAL ASHES SCORECARD

WAR OF WORDS GONE WRONG — 1994-95

THE 1994-95 CAMPAIGN OF ENGLAND STARTED WITH AMBITIOUS
AND PROVOKING PROCLAMATIONS, MOST OF WHICH BACKFIRED ON THE VISITORS.

STEVE WAUGH IS NOT ONLY THE MAIN CULPRIT IN THE SLEDGING CAMPAIGN MASTERMINDED BY OLD GRUMPY, HE WETS HIMSELF ROUTINELY ON FACING ANY BOWLER FASTER THAN GRAEME HICK.

I DON'T MIND WETTING MYSELF IF I'M GOING TO AVERAGE 80 AGAINST ENGLAND.

MANAGER KEITH FLETCHER TOUTED DEVON MALCOLM AS FASTER THAN LILLEE AND ALMOST RIVALLING THOMSON.

HE ENDED WITH 13 WICKETS AT 45 APIECE.

IT SOUNDS LIKE A HEAP OF S**T TO ME

THERE WAS BRUTAL 'ANALYSIS' OF THE ENGLISH FAILURES ...
THIS LED TO SOME OLD-FASHIONED WITCH-HUNT HINTING AT THE
LARGE PROPORTION OF OVERSEAS PLAYERS, INCLUDING SEVERAL NON-WHITES

THESE ARE NOT EXACTLY THINGS OF
THE PAST. RACIAL TAUNTS, QUESTIONS
ABOUT COMMITMENT EVEN THE CHOICE OF
SPORTING A BEARD HAVE OFTEN RAISED
THEIR MURKY HEADS.

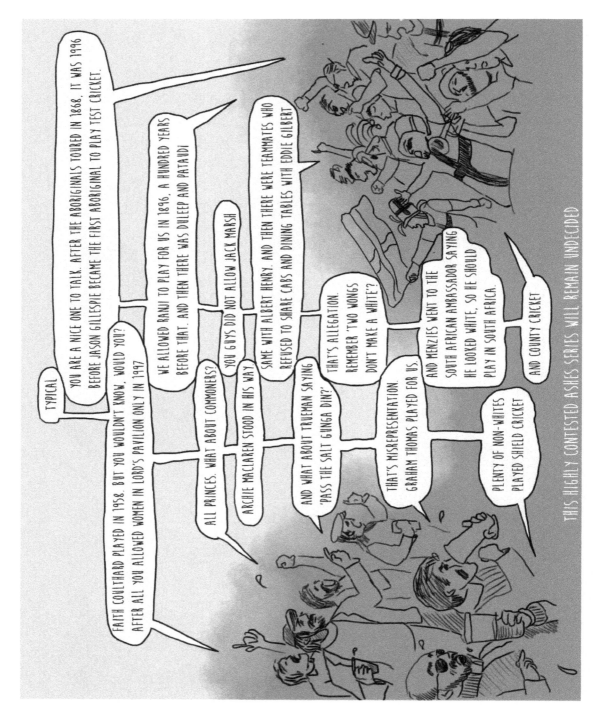

FLATTERING TO DECEIVE — 1997

STEVE WAUGH'S TWIN HUNDREDS AT OLD TRAFFORD COMBINED WITH MCGRATH (36 WICKETS) AND WARNE (29), AS THE TALE OF AUSSIE DOMINATION CONTINUED.

WHO'S WETTING HIMSELF NOW?

HOWEVER, ENGLAND HAD TAKEN AN UPPER HAND EARLY IN THE SERIES. MARK TAYLOR, THE NEW AUSTRALIAN CAPTAIN, HAD REACHED ENGLAND IN DREADFUL FORM.

A CENTURY, AND A LETTER OF CONFIDENCE FROM THE AUSTRALIAN PRIME MINISTER JOHN HOWARD, DID BOOST HIS MORALE BUT ENGLAND WENT UP 1-0 AT EDGBASTON.

HOWEVER, BY THE FIFTH TEST, AUSTRALIA HAD WON THE SERIES AND THE FIRST ENGLAND VICTORY HAD STARTED TO LOOK AS FAR BACK AS BOTHAM'S TEST OF 1981

AT THE OVAL, PHIL TUFNELL AND ANDY CADDICK BOWLED ENGLAND TO A CONSOLATION WIN. THE SERIES SCORELINE WAS 3-2, BUT DEFENDING 124 WAS SPECIAL.

SAME OLD SORRY SAGA — 1998-99

EVEN THE ABSENCE OF SHANE WARNE IN FOUR OF THE TESTS DID NOT HELP THE ENGLAND SIDE UNDER ALEC STEWART. REPLACEMENT LEGGIE STUART MACGILL CAPTURED 27 WICKETS. BOWLING IN TANDEM WITH WARNE AT SYDNEY, MACGILL PICKED UP 12 WICKETS TO WARNE'S 2, AS AUSTRALIA COMPLETED A 3-1 ROUT.

I HAVE IT ALL SET UP FOR YOU. JUST TAKE THAT BAGGY GREEN OFF AND BOWL LEG SPINNERS, AND THE POMMIES WILL BE SCURRYING FOR COVER.

SAY NO TO WAUGH

THE WAUGH TWINS AMASSED 891 RUNS BETWEEN THEM, AT AN AVERAGE OF 68.53.

THERE WAS SOME CHEER FOR ENGLAND. DARREN GOUGH CAPTURED A HATTRICK AT SYDNEY AND BOWLED HIS TEAM TO A MEMORABLE WIN AT MELBOURNE.

The Advertiser

England face the stinging reality that they no longer deserve a five-Test Ashes series.

BUT THE AUSTRALIAN PRESS WAS NOT CONVINCED.

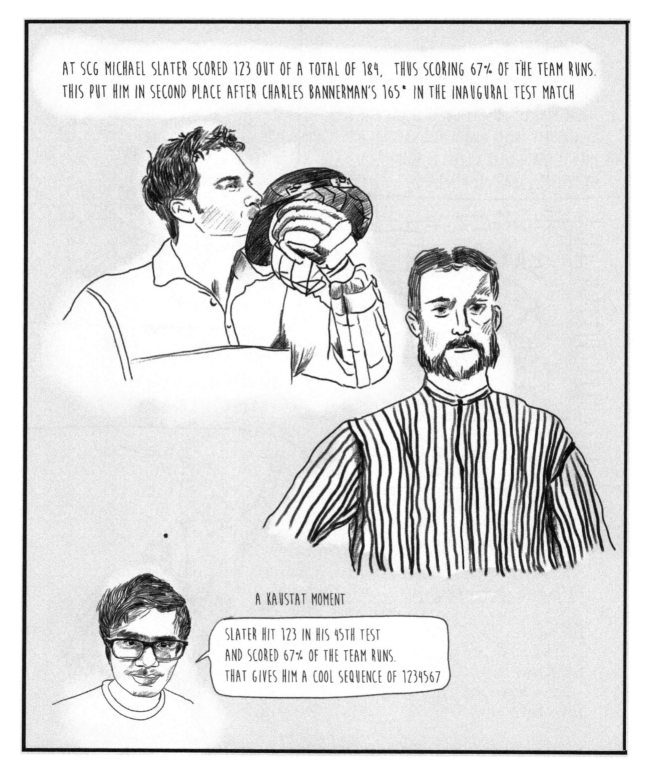

AT SCG MICHAEL SLATER SCORED 123 OUT OF A TOTAL OF 184, THUS SCORING 67% OF THE TEAM RUNS. THIS PUT HIM IN SECOND PLACE AFTER CHARLES BANNERMAN'S 165* IN THE INAUGURAL TEST MATCH

A KAUSTAT MOMENT

SLATER HIT 123 IN HIS 45TH TEST AND SCORED 67% OF THE TEAM RUNS. THAT GIVES HIM A COOL SEQUENCE OF 1234567

BY THE TIME OF THE NEXT ASHES, LORD'S HAD FINALLY BEEN HAULED OUT OF THE TROGLODYTIC AGES.

AT LAST YOU CAN WATCH ME MA

RACHEL HEYHOE-FLINT

1999

A GREAT TEAM ROLLS ON — 2001

IT WAS ONE OF THE GREATEST TEAMS THAT VISITED ENGLAND IN 2001. CAPTAIN STEVE WAUGH, THE BELLIGERENT ADAM GILCHRIST, THE CLASSY MARK WAUGH, THE ELEGANT DAMIEN MARTYN WITH THE BAT ...

... AND GLENN MCGRATH AND SHANE WARNE WITH THE BALL.

NOT SINCE DON BRADMAN IN 1948 HAD AN AUSTRALIAN CAPTAIN RETURNED HOME TO SUCH PAEANS OF PRAISE AS WAUGH.

JOHN WOODCOCK

IT WAS A SPORTING DECLARATION BY CAPTAIN GILCHRIST (STANDING IN FOR AN INJURED WAUGH AT HEADINGLEY) AND A MIRACULOUS UNBEATEN 173 BY MARK BUTCHER THAT ENABLED ENGLAND TO PULL ONE BACK TO END THE SERIES 4-1.

BATTERING CONTINUES — 2002-03

THE SERIES WAS DECIDED ON THE FIRST DAY ITSELF. TO BE PRECISE IT WAS HANDED OVER. NASSER HUSSAIN WON THE TOSS AT BRISBANE AND ASKED AUSTRALIA TO BAT FIRST. BY THE END OF THE FIRST DAY, MATTHEW HAYDEN WAS 186 NOT OUT AND THE HOSTS 364/2.

IS IT STILL DOING A BIT, SKIP?

MATTHEW HAYDEN (496 RUNS IN THE SERIES) AND JUSTIN LANGER (423) FORMED AN IMPREGNABLE WALL AT THE TOP, FOLLOWED BY RICKY PONTING (417). ADD TO THAT ADAM GILCHRIST SCORING 333 AT 55.50 WITH A STRIKE RATE OF 102.46. BY THE TIME AUSTRALIA WENT 4-0 UP IN THE SERIES AT MELBOURNE, THE MEDIA WAS ASKING UNCOMFORTABLE QUESTIONS.

HOWEVER, MICHAEL VAUGHAN BATTED LIKE A DREAM AGAINST MCGRATH, GILLESPIE, WARNE AND THE REST. 177 AT ADELAIDE AND 145 AT MELBOURNE WERE HIT IN LOSING CAUSES, BUT HIS 183 AT SYDNEY FINALLY BROUGHT ABOUT A CONSOLATION WIN FOR ENGLAND IN THE FINAL TEST. ANDY CADDICK'S 7 FOR 94 IN THE SECOND INNINGS HELPED TO MAKE IT IT 4-1.

PREMATURELY GREY? TRY BOWLING AGAINST THIS LINE UP.

WHILE THE ACTION ON THE FIELD WAS MONOTONOUSLY ONE-SIDED, THE BANTER WAS OFTEN SHARP AND FLEW FROM BOTH TEAMS.

F**K ME, LOOK WHO IT IS. MATE, WHAT ARE YOU DOING OUT HERE? THERE'S NO WAY YOU'RE GOOD ENOUGH TO PLAY FOR ENGLAND.

MAYBE NOT, BUT AT LEAST I'M THE BEST PLAYER IN MY FAMILY.

MARK WAUGH

JAMES ORMOND

NO, YOU CAN'T HAVE A GLASS OF WATER. WHAT DO YOU THINK THIS IS? A F***ING TEA PARTY?

ALLAN BORDER

ROBIN SMITH

YOU CAN'T F******* BAT.

ROBIN SMITH

MERV HUGHES

HEY MERV, WE MAKE A FINE PAIR. I CAN'T F******* BAT AND YOU CAN'T F******* BOWL.

YOU'RE A F***ING CHEAT

WHEN IN ROME, DEAR BOY

IAN HEALY

MIKE ATHERTON

```
1989        Aus 4 Eng 0
1990-91     Aus 3 Eng 0
1993        Aus 4 Eng 1
1994-95     Aus 3 Eng 1
1997        Aus 3 Eng 2
1998-99     Aus 3 Eng 1
2001        Aus 4 Eng 1
2002-03     Aus 4 Eng 1

Cumulative Ashes Head to Head
Tests - Aus 115 Eng 93
Series - Aus 30 Eng 27
```

ENG

AUS

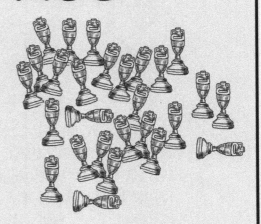

GROWING UP DURING THOSE YEARS WAS A NIGHTMARE FOR ENGLISH FANS.

NOT EVERYONE BELIEVED THAT THE POWER CENTRES OF CRICKET HAD SHIFTED, THOUGH ... WHEN IN 1993 IT WAS DECIDED THAT THE WORLD CUP WOULD BE HOSTED IN INDIA ...

THERE WAS A TIME, BEFORE MONEY AND POLITICS ENTERED THE EQUATION, WHEN THE COMMUNITY OF CRICKET NATIONS LOOKED NO FURTHER THAN UNITED KINGDOM TO STAGE THE WORLD CUP.

CHRISTOPHER MARTIN-JENKINS

THE AUSTRALIANS, HOWEVER, DID NOT REALLY CARE WHERE IT WAS HELD. THEY REACHED THE FINALS IN THE 1996 WORLD CUP IN THE SUBCONTINENT, WON IT IN ENGLAND IN 1999, IN 2003 IN SA AND WOULD GO ON TO WIN IN 2007 IN THE WEST INDIES. THEY DOMINATED ALL FORMATS.

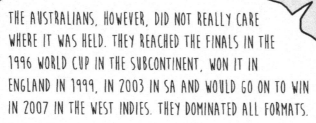

The Ashes

2005

AFTER YEARS OF ONE-SIDED CONTESTS AT LAST THERE WAS AN ASHES SERIES TO REMEMBER. THE EDGE-OF-THE-SEAT EXCITEMENT GENERATED BY THE 2005 TESTS RIVALLED THE FIRST GREAT TEST SERIES OF 1894-95.

DURING THE ENGLISH SUMMER, THERE SEEMED TO BE AN ENVELOPING BREATHLESS HUSH AS TEST MATCH AFTER TEST MATCH KEPT PRODUCING INTENSE DRAMA AND HEART-STOPPING FINISHES.

CRICKET REPLACED FOOTBALL IN THE COVER AND BACK PAGES OF NEWSPAPERS, CHANNEL 4 MOVED THE HIGHLIGHTS PACKAGE TO PRIME-TIME AND BBC RADIO FIVE LIVE BROADCAST ALL ITS DAY-TIME PROGRAMMES FROM THE OVAL DURING THE FINAL TEST.

TWO BOOKS ON THE SERIES WON THE WISDEN BOOK OF THE YEAR AWARD

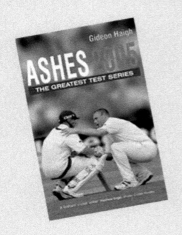
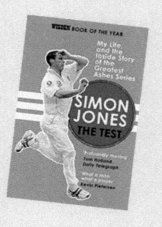

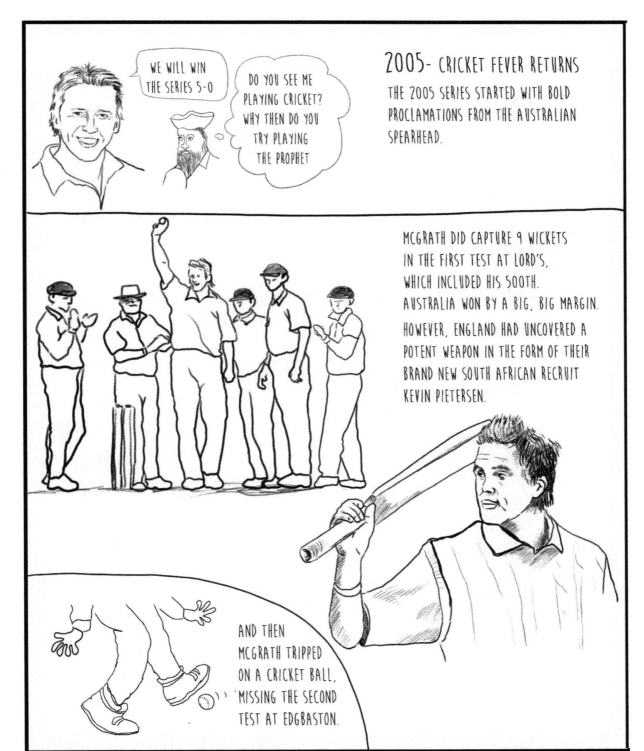

WE WILL WIN THE SERIES 5-0
DO YOU SEE ME PLAYING CRICKET? WHY THEN DO YOU TRY PLAYING THE PROPHET
2005- CRICKET FEVER RETURNS
THE 2005 SERIES STARTED WITH BOLD PROCLAMATIONS FROM THE AUSTRALIAN SPEARHEAD.
MCGRATH DID CAPTURE 9 WICKETS IN THE FIRST TEST AT LORD'S, WHICH INCLUDED HIS 500TH. AUSTRALIA WON BY A BIG, BIG MARGIN.
HOWEVER, ENGLAND HAD UNCOVERED A POTENT WEAPON IN THE FORM OF THEIR BRAND NEW SOUTH AFRICAN RECRUIT KEVIN PIETERSEN.
AND THEN MCGRATH TRIPPED ON A CRICKET BALL, MISSING THE SECOND TEST AT EDGBASTON.

IN THE SECOND TEST, FLINTOFF HIT 9 SIXES ACROSS 50S IN EACH INNINGS,..

...AND CAPTURED 7 WICKETS IN THE MATCH.

ENGLAND WON BY JUST TWO RUNS AFTER BRETT LEE AND MICHAEL KASPROWICZ HAD ADDED 59 FOR THE LAST WICKET.

AFTER KASPROWICZ FELL TO HARMISON, IT FELL UPON FLINTOFF TO END HIS DREAM MATCH IN A STERLING MANNER, CONSOLING LEE.

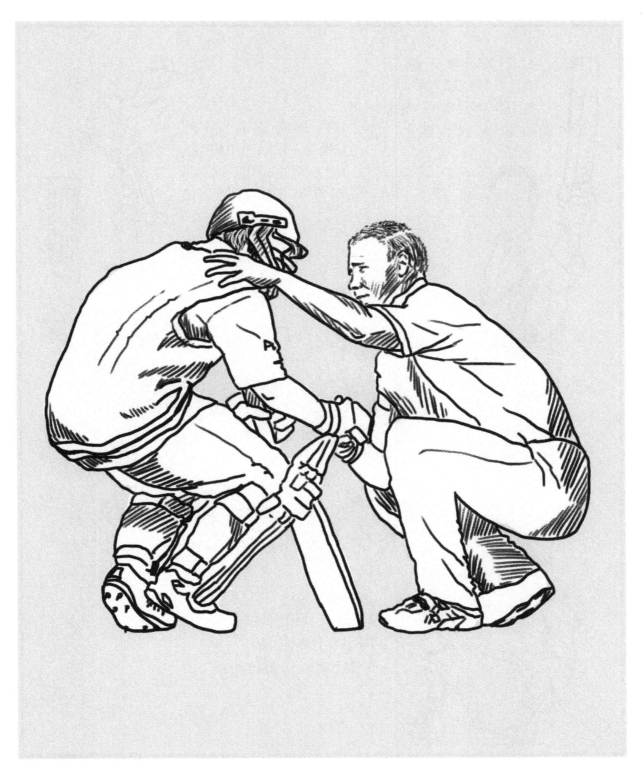

AT OLD TRAFFORD, IT WAS THE TALE OF TWO CAPTAINS. MICHAEL VAUGHAN SET ENGLAND UP WITH AN EXCELLENT 166.

RICKY PONTING HAD TO RAISE HIS GAME TO A DIFFERENT LEVEL TO KEEP AUSTRALIA AFLOAT, HITTING 156 IN THE FINAL INNINGS.

1 WICKET 1 BALL

AUSTRALIA SURVIVED WITH THE LAST PAIR LEE AND MCGRATH PLAYING OUT TIME.

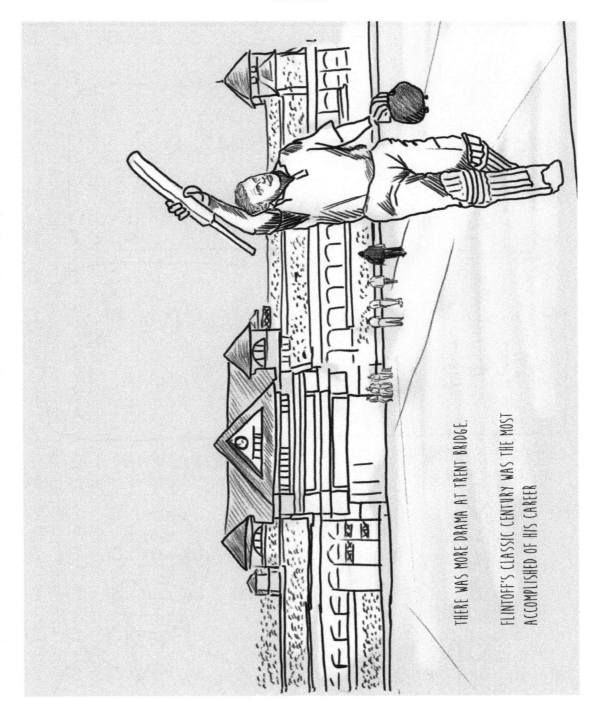

THERE WAS MORE DRAMA AT TRENT BRIDGE.

FLINTOFF'S CLASSIC CENTURY WAS THE MOST
ACCOMPLISHED OF HIS CAREER

The Ashes

IT COST AUSTRALIA THE ASHES AS PIETERSEN WENT ON TO HIT A MATCH SAVING 158

ENGLAND'S 2-1 TRIUMPH, THE RECOVERY OF THE ASHES AFTER 17 YEARS, PITCHFORKED CRICKET INTO THE LIMELIGHT, DISPLACING FOOTBALL IN THE BACKPAGES AND NEWS IN THE FRONT.

SPAR SUPERMARKET REPORTED A BOOST IN BEER AND FIZZY DRINKS SALES THROUGH THE SERIES.

DAVID BECKHAM TALKED ABOUT ASHES.

SHANE WARNE APPEARED ON GRAHAM NORTON'S BBC CHAT SHOW.

IT WAS A CONTEST TO REMEMBER. SEVERAL VERY GOOD ENGLISH CRICKETERS HIT THEIR PEAK FORM AT THE SAME TIME AND FOUGHT THE ALL-TIME GREATS OF THE AUSTRALIAN SIDE. TEST CRICKET AT ITS ABSOLUTE BEST.

THESE ARE THE MOMENTS ONE LIVES FOR.

AFTER ALL THOSE LONG YEARS OF FRUSTRATION, THE CELEBRATIONS OF THE ENGLISH FANS COULD BE UNDERSTOOD. HOWEVER, THE EUPHORIA WAS MOMENTARY.

TRUE. 2006-07 WITNESSED THE MOST EAGERLY ANTICIPATED ASHES SERIES IN HISTORY. BUT, IT ENDED IN A THUMPING 5-0 REVENGE FOR AUSTRALIA.
IN THEIR FINAL SERIES, GLENN MCGRATH AND SHANE WARNE WALKED INTO THE SUNSET AFTER INFLICTING THE FIRST ASHES WHITEWASH IN 86 YEARS.

2006-07 ONWARDS
MOVING TOWARDS HOME RULE

WITH ANOTHER GROUP OF SUPREME LEGENDS MOVING AWAY FROM THE SCENE, AUSTRALIA
TOOK A WHILE TO FORM A STABLE UNIT. DURING THESE YEARS, ENGLAND DOMINATED FOR A WHILE.

HOWEVER, WITH TIME THE TESTS FOLLOWED THE GLOBAL TREND OF UNPRECEDENTED HOME ADVANTAGE.
LIKE EVERY TOUR AROUND THE WORLD,
THE RESULTS BECAME HEAVILY LOADED IN FAVOUR OF THE HOME SIDE.
IN FACT, THE 2010-11 WAS THE LAST SERIES WON BY A VISITING SIDE.

NEW HEROES HAVE DAWNED. STEVE SMITH HOLDS CLAIM TO BEING THE MOST SUCCESSFUL BATSMAN
SINCE DON BRADMAN.
ALASTAIR COOK REWROTE RECORDS FOR RUNS AND CENTURIES FOR ENGLAND.
MITCHELL JOHNSON AND PAT CUMMINS BOWLED AS WELL AS ANY BOWLER IN THE HISTORY OF THE ASHES

2006-07 HURTLING FROM THE SUMMIT

THE SOJOURN AT THE TOP PROVED EXTREMELY BRIEF FOR ENGLAND. ANDREW FLINTOFF'S TEAM WERE BATTERED 5-0 IN THE FIRST EVER WHITEWASH SINCE 1920-21

ENGLAND WERE DAY-BY-DAY, DESTROYED, SUFFERING DEATH BY A THOUSAND CUTS.

MIKE SELVEY

EVEN SCORING 551 FOR 6, AS ENGLAND DID IN THE FIRST INNINGS OF THE SECOND TEST, WAS NOT ENOUGH TO STAVE OFF DEFEAT. THE AUSTRALIANS STUCK TO IT, THE GREAT MCGRATH-WARNE DUO KEPT TAKING WICKETS, AND ENGLAND KEPT COLLAPSING.

AFTER THE SERIES, JUSTIN LANGER JOINED MCGRATH AND WARNE IN TAKING FAREWELL, LEAVING MATTHEW HAYDEN ALONE TO START THE AUSTRALIAN INNINGS.

AND DAMIEN MARTYN SHOCKED THE WORLD BY RETIRING AFTER THE SECOND TEST MATCH OF THE SERIES.

I FINISHED FIRST!!

EVEN IN HIS FINAL SERIES, WARNE WAS IN HIS ELEMENT SLEDGING PAUL COLLINGWOOD.

YOU GOT AN MBE, RIGHT, PAUL? FOR SCORING 7 AT THE OVAL? YOU'RE AN EMBARRASSMENT

THIS SERIES WAS THE SWANSONG OF THE TWO
MOST SUCCESSFUL BOWLERS IN ASHES HISTORY.
WARNE (23) AND MCGRATH (21)
CAPTURED 44 WICKETS
BETWEEN THEM.

ASHES TESTS 36
WKTS 195
AVE 23.25

ASHES TESTS 30
WKTS 157
AVE 20.92

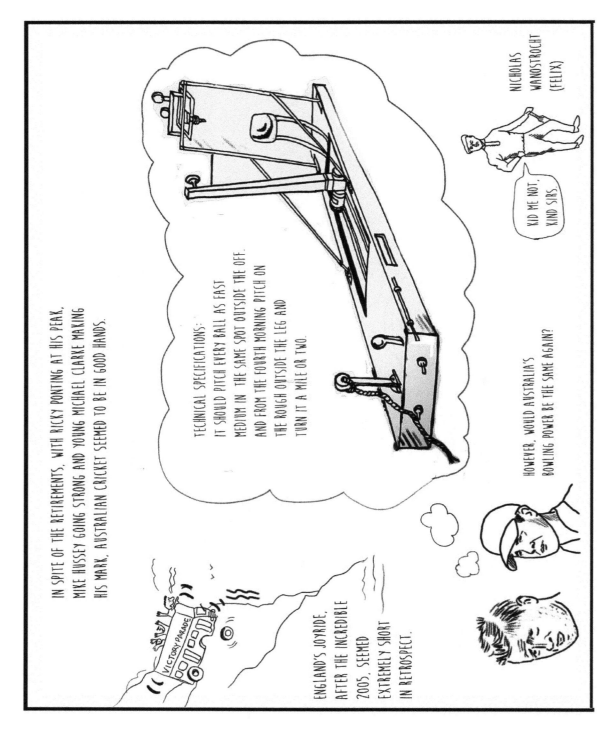

ANDREW STRAUSS LED ENGLAND TO A 2-1 WIN IN 2009. A DEFIANT 74 OVER FOUR HOURS AND 344 BALLS FROM COLLINGWOOD HELPED

NOW I KNOW WHY THEY GAVE YOU THE MBE. MOST BORING EVER.

AHEM !

ENGLAND DREW THE FIRST TEST AT CARDIFF WITH JAMES ANDERSON AND MONTY PANESAR PLAYING OUT THE FINAL 69 BALLS.

MAKE HIM HOLD HIS CELEBRATIONS, JIMMY.

AFTER THAT IT WAS A SEE-SAW SERIES WHICH ENGLAND CLINCHED WITH A BIG WIN AT THE OVAL, DEBUTANT JONATHAN TROTT SCORING A HUNDRED.

TALK OF HITTING THE GROUND TROTTING.

TROTT IS THE ONLY PLAYER TO SCORE A CENTURY ON TEST DEBUT IN AN ASHES MATCH IN THE LAST 25 YEARS

ENGLAND COULD AFFORD TO BE MAGNANIMOUS WHEN BRAD HADDIN WAS INJURED AFTER THE TOSS, ANDREW STRAUSS ALLOWED AUSTRALIA TO CHANGE THE SIDE AND PICK WICKETKEEPER GRAHAM MANOU INSTEAD.

YOU CAN KEEP THE CHANGE, AND THE CHANGE CAN KEEP.

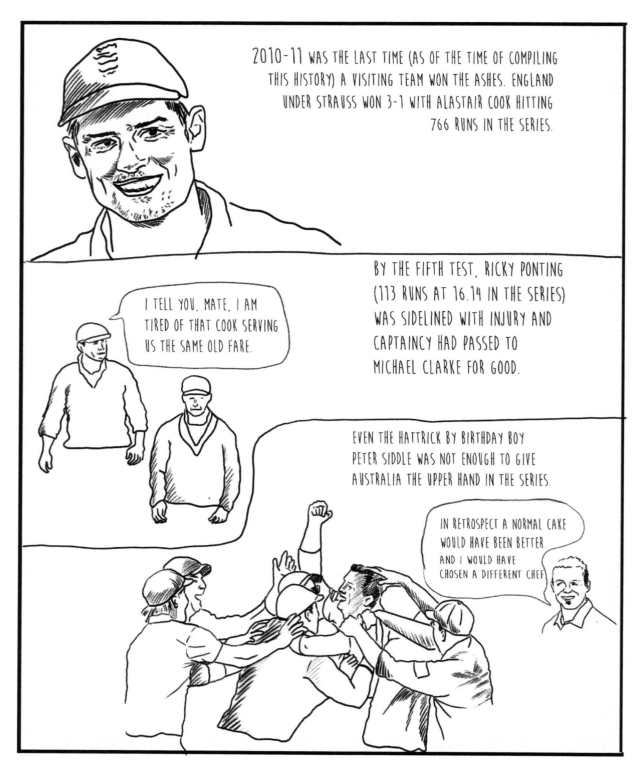

IN 2013, ALASTAIR COOK TOOK OVER THE CAPTAINCY FROM STRAUSS AND THE VISITING AUSSIES WERE DRUBBED 3-0. THE AUSTRALIAN BATTING HAD NO ANSWER TO THE BOWLING COMBINATION OF JAMES ANDERSON, STUART BROAD AND GRAEME SWANN.

WHILE RYAN HARRIS OUTDID HIMSELF FOR AUSTRALIA, IAN BELL STOOD LIKE A ROCK, SCORING 562 RUNS WITH THREE HUNDREDS.

WE'VE BELLED THE RHINO.

ASHTON AGAR'S 98 AT TRENT BRIDGE WAS THE THIRD TIME A NO.11 TOPSCORED IN AN ASHES INNINGS. THE OTHERS WERE FROM THE 19TH CENTURY - FRED SPOFFORTH (50 AT MELBOURNE, 1885) AND TOM MCKIBBIN (16 AT THE OVAL, 1896)

THE AUSSIES, AS YOU SEE, ARE EASY. NOW, KP ... THAT'S A DIFFERENT STORY.

JONATHAN TROTT RETURNED HOME AFTER THE FIRST TEST. JOHNSON'S PACE AND HIS FRAGILE STATE OF MIND COMPOUNDED THE PROBLEMS.

THE HEADLINES WERE IRRESPONSIBLE AND SCATHING —

It will be difficult for any England captain to trust Jonathan Trott again

TROTT MUST ACCEPT TEAM-MATES AND OPPONENTS WILL FEEL HE DID A RUNNER.

IT JUST UNDERLINES THE INSENSITIVITY OF TESTOSTERONE-BASED SPORTS REPORTING TOWARDS MENTAL HEALTH.

THE 2015 SCORELINE SEEMED CLOSER THAN THE SERIES ACTUALLY WAS.

ONE OF THE BEST YOUNG BATSMEN OF THE WORLD, JOE ROOT, SCORED 134 AND 60 AS ENGLAND WON THE FIRST TEST MATCH AT CARDIFF. STEVE SMITH RESPONDED WITH 215 AT LORD'S AS AUSTRALIA DREW LEVEL.

THEREAFTER IT WAS A ONE SIDED TALE. JAMES ANDERSON AND STEVEN FINN ROUTED AUSTRALIA AT EDGBASTON, AND AT TRENT BRIDGE, STUART BROAD DECIMATED THEM FOR 60 WITH FIGURES OF 8 FOR 15.

ANOTHER SMITH HUNDRED WAS INSTRUMENTAL IN THE AUSTRALIAN WIN AT THE OVAL, BUT THE SERIES HAD ALREADY BEEN DECIDED. THE MOST DISAPPOINTING BIT WAS THAT NONE OF THE FIVE TESTS WAS WELL CONTESTED.

YOU HAVE TO MAKE DO WITH THE TRAM, AND NOT THE EAST MIDLAND EXPRESS. AFTER ALL, NOTTINGHAMSHIRE FAST BOWLERS START FROM LARWOOD.

YEAH BUT THIS WILL BE A BROAD GAUGE

STUART BROAD

BY THE END OF THE SECOND DAY OF EACH MATCH WE ALWAYS KNEW WHO WAS GOING TO WIN; SOMETIMES THAT WAS OBVIOUS BY THE END OF THE FIRST DAY; AT NOTTINGHAM BY THE FIRST INTERVAL

VIC MARKS

2017-18 SAW AUSTRALIAN CRICKETERS OVERCOME A MAJOR PAYMENT ISSUE. FOR A LONG TIME IT WAS NOT CLEAR WHETHER THE BIG STARS WOULD PLAY AT ALL.

AS THE AUSTRALIAN SITUATION IMPROVED ENGLAND DEALT A DEADLY BLOW BY ONE OF THEIR TRUMP CARDS. STAR ALL-ROUNDER BEN STOKES GOT INTO TROUBLE FOR GETTING INTO FISTICUFFS OUTSIDE A BAR AND WAS RULED OUT OF THE SERIES AS THE DISCIPLINARY PROCESS WENT ON.

IN A RAIN AFFECTED SECOND TEST AT LORD'S ENGLAND UNLEASHED JOFRA ARCHER AT SMITH AIMING FOR HIS BODY

I KNOW THE FEELING. MAKE THE GAME TOO ONE-SIDED, AND THEY WILL FORGET THE STUMPS AND BOWL AT YOU.

RELAX. YOU'RE A DEBUTANT, THEY'VE WORKED HARD ON YOUR ELIGIBILITY FOR ENGLAND ...

THE KEY IS STAYING WITHIN THE RULES OF THE GAME. BESIDES, YOU LOOK BOYISH AND INNOCENT, AND DON'T WEAR A HARLEQUIN CAP.

CONCUSSION SUBSTITUTE MARNUS LABUSCHAGNE SEEMED TO HAVE STEPPED RIGHT INTO SMITH'S SHOES. AUSTRALIA HUNG ON TO THE LEAD.

LIKE FOR LIKE IS ALL VERY WELL, BUT LABUSCHAGNE DIDN'T HAVE TO TAKE THAT LITERALLY.

HOWEVER, AFTER SCORING ANOTHER 80 IN THE FIRST INNINGS AT THE OVAL, IN THE FINAL INNINGS OF THE TOUR, SMITH'S BAT FAILED HIM. ENGLAND SQUARED THE SERIES 2-2

WHEN THE BATTLE'S LOST AND WON

ONLY THE SIXTH DRAWN SERIES IN THE HISTORY OF THE ASHES

THE WAGON WHEELS

The Ashes

2005	Eng 2 Aus 1
2006-07	Aus 5 Eng 0
2009	Eng 2 Aus 1
2010-11	Eng 3 Aus 1
2013	Eng 3 Aus 0
2014-15	Aus 5 Eng 0
2015	Eng 3 Aus 2
2017-18	Aus 4 Eng 0
2019	Eng 2 Aus 2

Cumulative Ashes Head to Head
Tests - Aus 136 Eng 108
Series - Aus 33 Eng 32

ENG

AUS

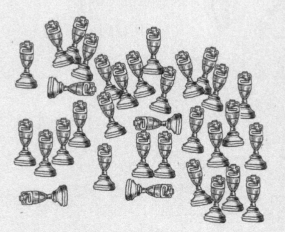

2020-21   Led by new captain Pat Cummins, and powered by a 148-ball 152 by Travis Head, Australia blew England away in three and a half days at Brisbane

By the time they were bowled out for 68 on the third morning at Melbourne to lose by an innings and thereby surrender the series, the press was scathing

Ashes-winning captain Ray Illingworth passed away on the eve of the Boxing Day Test

The England side wore black bands down under...

The Ashes

MEANWHILE SCOTT BOLAND, FAST BOWLER WITH INDIGENOUS ORIGINS, WON THE JOHNNY MULLAGH MEDAL BY BEING PLAYER OF THE MATCH IN THE BOXING DAY TEST. HE PICKED UP 6/7 ON DEBUT

EVEN IN NON-CONTESTS SOME DID THEIR BEST TO CHAMPION THE CAUSE OF THE ASHES

THE ANGUISH OVER ENGLAND'S IMPLOSION IN AUSTRALIA SHOWS HOW MUCH PEOPLE LOVE THE ASHES AND TEST CRICKET. THE ANGER ISN'T JUST ABOUT THE HUGE DEFEAT. THAT'S THE ONE REASSURING NOTE.

Friday, 7 January

Courageous Stokes defies injury to put pressure back on Australia

| CRICKET

AUS 416/8 DEC.
ENG 132/4
STOKES 43*

AFTER USMAN KHWAJA'S TWIN HUNDREDS,

THEY'LL ASK US TO KEEP WICKETS NOW

NEW-BALL PARTNERS ANDERSON AND BROAD BATTED OUT THE LAST FEW MINUTES TO SAVE ENGLAND FROM DEFEAT AT SYDNEY

AT HOBART THE 4-0 ROUT WAS COMPLETED WITH HEAD GETTING ANOTHER HUNDRED AND ENGLAND SUFFERING ANOTHER CAPITULATION

THANK GOD IT'S OVER!

2021-22 Aus 4 Eng 0

Cumulative Ashes Head to Head
Tests - Aus 140 Eng 108
Series - Aus 34 Eng 32

ENG

AUS

THE DISAPPOINTMENT WAS PALPABLE ...
BUT THE DEGREE OF DISPARAGEMENT HAS BEEN DIFFERENT

PAKISTAN HAVE LOST 14 OF THEIR LAST
14 TESTS IN AUSTRALIA

ENGLAND HAVE LOST 13 OF THEIR LAST
15 TESTS IN AUSTRALIA

SOMEBODY'S GOT TO GIVE THEM A KICK
UP THE BUM. CRICKET AUSTRALIA HAVE
GOT TO START SAYING 'LISTEN IF
THINGS DON'T IMPROVE WE WILL
STOP WITH THE INVITES

THE AUSTRALIA-VERSUS-ENGLAND SERIES
HAS OFTEN BEEN FRUSTRATINGLY ONE-SIDED.
AMPLE EMOTION OF THE SORT VISIBLE IN
IND-SA TESTS HAS NOTABLY BEEN MISSING
FROM AN ASHES CONTEST

Scene: IMC - DGB
Take: 6997

NOW LET ME TELL YOU ABOUT
HOW BRADMAN STOOD IN THE
WAY OF OUR GETTING DECENT
PAY IN THE 1970S ...

SINCE MIKE GATTING'S TEAM WON THE ASHES IN 1986-87, THE HEAD TO HEAD BETWEEN THESE TWO TEAMS HAVE NOT REALLY INDICATED THE BEST OF RIVALRIES. THE RESULTS HAVE BEEN WAY TOO ONE-SIDED

IND-AUS, IND-SA, IND-ENG AND ENG-SA HAVE PROVIDED MUCH CLOSER AND MORE BALANCED CONTESTS

UNFORTUNATELY IND-PAK DON'T PLAY EACH OTHER ANY MORE

Aus - Eng	53-22	Aus - Ind	23-22	Eng - SA	18-16	NZ-Ind	9-12
		Aus - SA	23-15	Eng - Ind	19-20	NZ-Pak	11-15
		SA- Ind	17-15	Eng - Pak	13-18	NZ-SL	12-9
		Ind-Pak	5-5	Pak-SL	15-15		

ASHES IS CRICKET'S SIMPSONS .. PEAKED ABOUT SEASON 10, BUT STILL CONTINUOUS IN SEASON 33

BUT THE ASHES HAS SUCH A BIG ROLE IN THE HISTORY OF CRICKET. DO THE LAST FEW YEARS NEGATE ALL THAT?

1987 TO 2022 CONSTITUTE 35 YEARS. THAT IS 24% OF THE HISTORY OF TEST CRICKET. 1376 OF THE 2449 TEST MATCHES, 56% OF THE TOTAL NUMBER OF TEST MATCHES PLAYED. THAT IS TOO LONG FOR A CONTEST TO BE ONE-SIDED. HISTORY CANNOT REMAIN STAGNANT ... IT HAS TO EVOLVE WITH TIMES

WE KNOW IT IS THE INVENTOR OF CRICKET AGAINST WHAT CAN BE CONSIDERED THE BEST TEAM OVER CRICKET HISTORY. HOWEVER, ARE WE SO KEEN ABOUT THE COMPARATIVE FORTUNES OF GREECE AND USA IN THE OLYMPICS MEDALS TALLY?

BUT ISN'T THIS BOOK ABOUT THE ENORMOUSLY RICH PAST OF THE ASHES? TO BE HONEST, IT IS ON THIS JOURNEY THAT I HAVE REALISED THAT THE HISTORY OF THE ASHES IS SOMEWHAT MORE THAN BOYCOTT, BOTHAM, CHAPPELLI, RICHIE BENAUD, MESSERSCHMITT, BODYLINE AND BRADMAN

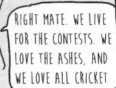

THE HISTORY OF THE ASHES WILL REMAIN AS RICH AS EVER. HOWEVER, HISTORIES OF OTHER NATIONS AND THEIR CRICKETING RIVALRIES HAVE EVOLVED. THEY ARE WORTH EVERY BIT OF ATTENTION AND CANNOT BE NEGLECTED. WE CANNOT PRETEND THAT IT IS STILL ONLY ENGLAND AND AUSTRALIA PLAYING TEST CRICKET. THERE IS COMPETITION, WHETHER ONE LIKES IT OR NOT. THE BEST WAY TO DEAL WITH THIS IS TO ENSURE THAT THE SERIES BETWEEN ENGLAND AND AUSTRALIA BECOMES MORE OF A RIVETING CONTEST THAN TRYING TO RIDE ON THE HYPE OF HISTORY

RIGHT MATE. WE LIVE FOR THE CONTESTS. WE LOVE THE ASHES, AND WE LOVE ALL CRICKET

The Ashes

SERIES LOOK UP

SERIES LOOK UP

Extra cover

For heaven's sake refer Cricinfo, Cricketarchive or stack your shelves with Wisdens

SELECTED BIBLIOGRAPHY

SELECTED BIBLIOGRAPHY

Alston, Rex; Test Commentary; Stanley Paul, 1956
Arlott, JL ; Two summers at the Tests; Pavilion Books, 1986
Arlott, JL and Brogden, Stanley; The first Test Match ; Phoenix House, 1950
Arnold, Michael; Bodyline Hypocrisy; Pitch Publishing, 2013
Atherton, Mike; Atherton's Ashes; Simon & Schuster, 2009
Barnes, SG; The Ashes Blaze; Kimber, 1955
Barnes, SG; Eye on The Ashes; Kimber, 1953
Bartley, Nehemiah; Opals and agates or Scenes under the Southern Cross and the Magellans; Gordon & Gooch, 1892
Batchelor, DS; The Picture Post book of the Tests; P Hutton, 1955
Batchelor, DS; The Test matches of 1964; The Commission, 1964
Bedser, Alec; May's Men in Australia; Stanley Paul, 1959
Benaud, Richie; Spin me a Spinner; Hodder & Stoughton, 1963
Benaud, Richie; A Tale of Two Tests; Hodder & Stoughton, 1962
Berry, Scylde; Cricket's Burning Passion; Methuen, 2006
Beston, RD; St Ivo and the Ashes; Australian Press Agency, 1883
Birley, Derek; Social History of English Cricket; Aurum, 2013
Bonnell, Max; How Many More Are Coming? The Short Life of Jack Marsh; Walla Walla Press, 2003
Border, AR; Ashes Glory: Allan Border's own story; Swan Publishing, 1989
Botham, IT; The incredible Tests, 1981; Pelham Books, 1981
Bowes, Bill; Aussies and Ashes; Stanley Paul, 1961
Bradman, Don; Farewell to Cricket; Hodder & Stoughton, 1950
Brearley, Mike; The Ashes Retained; Hodder & Stoughton, 1979
Brearley, Mike; Pheonix from the Ashes; Hodder & Stoughton,1982
Brodribb, Gerald; The Croucher; London Magzaine Editions, 1974
Brown, LH; Victor Trumper and the 1902 Australians; Secker & Warburg, 1981
Cardus, Neville; Australian Summer; Souvenir Press, 1987
Cardus, Neville; A Cricketer's Book; Grant Richards, 1929
Cardus, Neville; Autobiography; Collins, 1975
Carey, Michael; The Battle for the Ahses: The Daily Telegraph Story of the 1985 Tests; The Daily Telegraph, 1985
Carr, Arthur; Cricket with the lid off; Hutchinson, 1935
Chalke, Stephen; At the Heart of English Cricket; Fairfeld Books, 2001
Chalke, Stephen; No Coward Soul; Fairfield Books, 2003
Chalke, Stephen; Tom Cartwight: The Flame Still Burns; Fairfield Books, 2007
Chalke, Stephen; Ken Taylor: Drawn to Sport; Fairfield Books, 2006
Chappell, GS and Frith, David; Ashes '77; Angus & Robertson, 1978
Clarke, John Campbell; With England in Australia: the MCC tour 1965-66; Stanley Paul, 1966
Clarke, John Campbell; The Australians in England 1964; Stanley Paul, 1964
Clinton, Brian; The Art of Bradman; Sportsbooks, 2005
Colman, Mike; Eddie Gilbert; ABC Books, 2002
Compton, DCS; In Sun and in Shadow; Stanley Paul, 1952
Crawford, JN; Trip to Kangaroo Land; Cricket Offices, 1909
Cutler, Norman; Behind the Tests: the story behind the 1953 Test matches; Putnam, 1953
Dhole, Pradip; Billy Midwinter; CricketMASH, 2021

Eager, Patrick and Ross, Alan; A Summer to Remember; Collins, 1981
Eager, Patrick and Ross, Alan; An Australian Summer: the recovery of the Ashes 1985; Kingwood Press, 1985
Eager, Patrick and Ross, Alan; Tour of tours: Border's victorious Australians of 1989; Hodder & Stoughton, 1989
Engel, Matthew; Ashes '85; Pelham Books, 1985
Fender, PGH ; Defending The Ashes; Chapman & Hall, 1921
Fender, PGH ; Turn of the Wheel; Faber & Faber, 1929
Fender, PGH ; Kissing the Rod; Chapman & Hall, 1934
Ferriday, Patrick; Before the Lights Went Out; Von Krumm Publishing, 2012
Fingleton, Jack; Cricket Crisis; Cassell, 1946
Fingleton, Jack; Brown and Company; Collins, 1951
Fingleton, Jack; Four Chukkas to Australia; Heineman, 1960
Fingleton, Jack; Brightly fades the Don; Pavilion Books, 1985
Fingleton, Jack; The Ashes Crown the year; Pavilion Books, 1986
Foot, David; Wally Hammond: The Reasons Why; Ronson Books, 1996
Fortune, Charles; The Australians in England, 1961; Hale, 1961
Frith, David; Stoddy's Mission; Allen & Unwin, 1994
Frith, David; Bodyline Autopsy; Aurum Press, 2003
Frith, David; Australia Versus England : A Pictorial History of Every Test Match since 1877; Willow Books, 1986
Frith, David; The Trailblazers; Boundary Books, 1999
Frith, David; The Ashes '79; Angus & Robertson, 1979
Frith, David; Archie Jackson The Keats of Cricket; Pavilion, 1987
Frith, David; Paddington Boy; CricketMASH, 2021
Geras, Norman and Holiday, Ian; Ashes 97: Two views from the Boundary; Tisbury, 1997
Gibson, Alanm; Jackson's Year; Sportsman's Book Club, 1966
Gilligan, AER; Australian Challenge; Abelard Schuman, 1956
Gilligan, AER; Collins's Men; Arrowsmith, 1926
Grace, EM; The trip to Australia: scapes from the diary of one of the twelve; WH Knight, 1864
Haigh, Gideon; One Summer Every Summer: An Ashes Journal; Melbourne Text Publishing, 1995
Haigh, Gideon; Ashes 2005: The Greatest Test Series; Aurum Press, 2006
Haigh, Gideon; The Big Ship; Allen & Unwin, 2012
Haigh, Gideon; The Mystery Spinner; Aurum Press, 2002
Haigh, Gideon; Summer Game; The Text Publishing Company, 1999
Haigh, Gideon; Ashes 2011; Aurum Press, 2011
Haigh, Gideon; Ashes to Ashes; Viking, 2014
Haigh, Gideon; The Ultimate Test; Aurum Press, 2009
Haigh, Gideon and Frith, David; Inside Story: Unlocking Australian Cricket's Archives; News Custom Publishing, 2007
Harris, Bruce; Ashes Triumphant; Hutchinson, 1955
Harris, Bruce; Cricket triump: England versus Australia 1953; Hutchinson, 1953
Harris, Bruce; Defending The Ashes, 1956; Hutchinson, 1956
Hobbs, JB; Recovering the Ashes; Pitman, 1912
Hobbs, JB; The Fight for the Ashes, 1932-33; Harrap, 1933
Hughes, Margaret; The Long Hop; Stanley Paul, 1955
Illingworth, Ray; Yorkshire and Back; Queen Anne Press, 1980
Jardine, DR; In Quest of the Ashes; Hutchinson, 1933
Jardine, DR; Ashes and Dust; Hutchinson, 1934
Johnson, Ian; Cricket at the Crossroads; Cassell, 1957

Kimber, Jarrod; Test Cricket: The Unauthorised Biography; Hardie Grant Books, 2015
Kippax, Alan; Anti-Bodyline; Hurst & Blackett, 1933
Knox, Malcolm; Bradman's War; Penguin Random House, 2012
Knox, Malcolm; Never a Gentleman's Game; Hardie Grant, 2012
Laker, Jim; Over to Me; Frederick Muller, 1960
Laker, Jim; Spinning Around The World; The Sportsman's Book Club, 1959
Laker, Jim; The Australian Tour of 1961; Frederick Muller, 1961
Larwood, Harold; Body-line? ; Elkin Matthews & Marrot, 1933
Laver, Frank; An Australian cricketer on tour; Chapman & Hall, 1905
Lee, Alan; A Pitch in Both Camps; Stanley Paul, 1979
Lester, Roy; The fight for the Ashes in 1953; Flagstaff, 1953
Mackay, Ken; Quest for the Ashes; Pelham, 1966
Mailey, AA; And then came Larwood; Sportsman's Book Club, 1951
Mailey, AA; Mailey's googlies; Graphic Publications, 1921
Mailey, AA; 10 for 66 and All That; Phoenix, 1959
Mant, Gilbert; Cuckoo in the Bodyline Nest; Kangaroo Press, 1992
Martin-Jenkins, Christopher; Assault on the Ashes; McDonald and Jane's, 1975
Martin-Jenkins, Christopher; The Jubilee Tests; MacDonald and Jane, 1977
Mason, RC; Ashes in the Mouth; Hambledon Press, 1982
Mason, Ronald; Warwick Armstrong's Australians; Epsworth, 1971
McCrery, Nigel; The Coming Storm; Pen and Sword Military, 2017
McCrery, Nigel; Final Wicket; Pen and Sword Military, 2015
Melford, Michael; Botham rekindles the Ashes; The Daily Telegraph, 1981
Midwinter, Eric; Class Peace; ACS, 2017
Miller, Keith; Cricket from the grandstand; Oldbourne, 1959
Miller, Keith and Whitington, Richard; Catch; Latimer House, 1951
Morris, Arthur and Landsberg, Pat; Operation Ashes; Hale, 1956
Moyes, AG; The Fight for The Ashes; Harrap, 1951
Moyes, AG; Benaud & Co; Angus & Robertson, 1959
Moyes, AG; With the MCC in Australia 1962-63; Angus & Robertson, 1963
Mulvaney, John; Cricket Walkabout; Macmillan, 1988
Munns, Joy; Beyond Reasonable Doubt; The Author, 1994
Noble, MA; Gilligan's Men; Chapman & Hall, 1925
Noble, MA; The Fight for the Ashes, 1928-29; Harrap, 1929
O'Reilly, WJ; Cricket Task Force; T Werner Laurie, 1951
Pardon, Charles; The Australians in England: a complete record of the cricket tour of 1884; JW McKenzie, 1984
Peebles, Ian; The Fight for The Ashes 1958-59; Angus & Robertson, 1959
Ponting, Ricky; Ashes Diary: 2005; Harpersport, 2005
Rae, Simon; WG Grace A Life; Faber & Faber, 1999
Ranjitsinhji, KS; With Stoddart's team in Australia; James Bowden, 1898
Rice, Jonathan; The Fight for the Ashes, 2001; Methuen, 2001
Robinson, Ray; Between Wickets; Collins, 1946
Robinson, Ray; From the Boundary; Collins, 1951
Roebuck, Peter; Ashes to Ashes; Kingswood Press, 1987
Rosenwater, Irving; Sir Donald Bradman; Batsford, 1978
Ross, Alan; Australia 55; M Joseph, 1955
Ross, Alan; Australia 63; Eyre & Spottiswoode, 1963
Ross, Alan; Cape Summer and the Australians in England; Constable, 1986
Ross, Gordon; Three Years On; NatWest Bank, 1983
Royle, Vernon; Lord Harris's Team in Australia 1878-79; MCC & JW McKenzie, 2001

Rushton, William; Marylebone versus the World; Pavilion Books, 1987
Sengupta, Arunabha; Apartheid: A Point to Cover; CricketMASH, 2020
Shaw, Alfred and Shrewsbury, Arthur; Cricket: Shaw and Shrewsbury's team in Australia 1884-85; Shaw & Shrewsury, 1885
Simpson, Bobby; The Australians in England 1968; Stanley Paul, 1968
Sissons, Ric and Stoddart, Brian; Cricket and Empire; Allen & Unwin, 1984
Smith, Rick   ; The Cricket Brawl; Applebooks, 1995
Smith, Rick and Williams, Ron; WG Down Under; Applebooks, 1994
Smith, Sydney; With the 15th Australian XI; ET Kibblewhite, 1922
Snow, John; Cricket Rebel; Hamlyn, 1976
Swanton, EW; Swanton in Australia with MCC 1946-1975; Collins, 1975
Swanton, EW; Elusive Victory; Hodder & Stoughton, 1951
Swanton, EW; The Ashes in Suspense; Daily Telegraph, 1963
Swanton, EW; The Test matches of 1953; Daily Telegraph, 1953
Swanton, EW; Gubby Allen: Man of Cricket; Hutchinson, 1985
Trevor, Major PCW; With the MCC in Australia (1907-1908); A Rivers, 1908
Tyson, Frank; In the Eye of the Typhoon; Parrs Wood Press, 1955
Tyson, Frank; Test of Nerves; Manark Pty, 1975
Tyson, Frank; The Centenary Test; Pelham, 1977
Valentine, Barry; Cricket's Dawn that Died; Breedon Books, 1991
Wakefield, BJ; Bradman the Great; Mainstream, 1999
Warner, PF; Cricket Across the Seas; Longman's, 1903
Warner, PF; How we recovered The Ashes; Chapman & Hall, 1904
Warner, PF; England v Australia, the record of the tour; Mills & Boon, 1912
Warner, PF; The Fight for the Ashes, 1926; Harrap, 1926
Wellings, EM; No Ashes for England; Evans Bros, 1951
Wellings, EM; The Ashes Thrown Away; Dymock's, 1959
Wellings, EM; Dexter versus Benaud; Bailey Bros & Swinten, 1963
Wellings, EM; Simpson's Australians; Hale, 1964
West, Peter; The fight for the Ashes, 1953; Harrap, 1953
West, Peter; The fight for the Ashes, 1956; Sportsman's Book Club, 1957
West, Peter; Clean Sweep; WH Allen, 1987
Whimpress, Bernard; Amazing Grace; Flanders University of South Australia, 1991
Wilde, Simon; Ranji: The Strange Genius of Ranjitsinhji; Gardner Books, 2005
Wilde, Simon; England: The Biography: The Story of English Cricket; Simon & Schuster, 2018
Willis, Ronald; Cricket's Biggest Mystery: the Ashes; Littleworth Press, 1983
Woodward, Ian; Cricket Not War; SMK, 1994
Woolmer, Bob; Bob Woolmer's Art and Science of Cricket; Random Hous Struik, 2008

Websites, Magazines and Others:

Cricinfo	The Cricketer
Cricketarchive	Cricket: Weekly Record of the Game
Cricketcountry	ACS Journals
Cricketweb	Wisden Almanacks
Cricmash	Hours In the British Library
The site of Old Ebor	John McKenzie's shelves
ACS Website	

The Ashes

ACKNOWLEDGEMENTS

Maha and Arun would like to thank:

The crack team of
Abhishek Mukherjee, Sreeram Iyer, Mayukh Ghosh and Michael Jones
for sharing their expertise and carrying out rigorous fact checks.

Pradip Dhole and Kartikeya Date for their inputs.
David Frith for opening his incredible vaults of knowledge.
David Squires for going through the book and providing his comments
Peter Wynne-Thomas for spending two full days on the material– when
few such days remained.
Stephen Chalke for his constant encouragement and for providing the
thoughtful foreword.
Neil Robinson for his time and the sparkling preface.
Patrick Ferriday for his time and suggestions
Martin Chandler for digging out some rather rare reference photographs
Kaustubh Gudipati for his incredible facility for trivia and youthful sincerity
Harini Vinayakam for her unparalled enthusiasm and water-tight editing
Austin Coutinho for taking the time to guide us in the early stages of the book

Apart from that Arun would like to acknowledge the help received at
various stages of the preparation of the book from:
John McKenzie
Christoph Saunders
Tony and Elaine Ring
Esther Greene
Sebastian Behringer
Anna Dragstra
Marten Kroese
Louke Spigt
Meha
and
Coco

Maha would like to express her thanks additionally to:
Her mom, Santha
Vignesh
Satish
Ajju
Srividya
and
MCC Gumbal

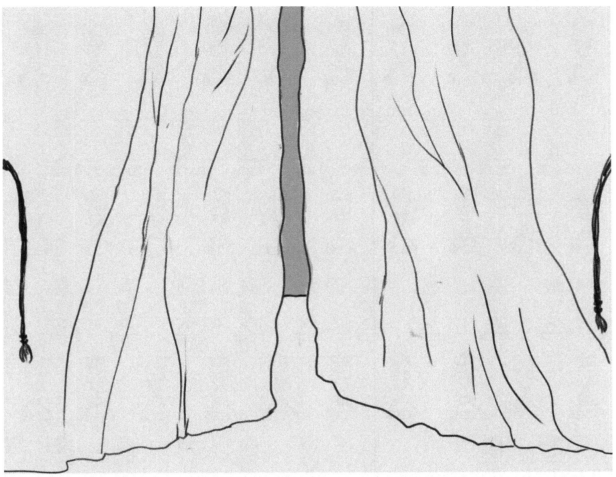

Arunabha Sengupta is a cricket historian, analyst
and writer for numerous cricket publications.
His previous cricket books include
Sachin and Azhar at Cape Town (co-author),
Apartheid: A Point to Cover,
and the cricket-based historical mystery novel
Sherlock Holmes and the Birth of The Ashes.

Maha is a London based artist and illustrator. .
Her work includes illustration for sports websites,
books and publications.
She also paints portraits and has been shortlisted
at the National Open art and more recently at
the Football Art Prize. This is her flirst book.

The Ashes